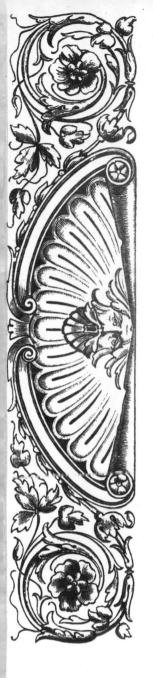

A 366 DAY CREATIVE PLANNER
BY
TERCES ENGELHART
DESIGNED BY JON MARRO

PLENTY OF TIME
A 366 DAY CREATIVE PLANNER
BY TERCES ENGELHART

PRINTED IN CHINA
ROBERT M. CLARK
NORCAL PRINTING, INC
RMCSLAP@AOL.COM
PRINTED ON RECYCLED PAPER USING VEGETABLE-BASED INKS.

ISBN: 978-1-60643-965-4

PUBLISHED BY:
ETERNAL PRESENCE
160 14TH STREET
SAN FRANCISCO, CA 94103
WWW.WITHTHECURRENT.COM
WWW.CAFEGRATITUDE.COM

BOOK DESIGN BY JON MARRO
WWW.FIREHYDRANT-RED.COM
WWW.BLENDAPPAREL.COM
ADDITIONAL MARCH, MAY, AUGUST, & NOVEMBER COLLAGE ASSISTANCE FROM THE LOVELY MARY LAUREL BURT
LOVINGLY/FIERCELY EDITED BY AMANDA SAYRE CASKEY

PLENTY OF TIME IS DEDICATED TO THE WISE SOUL IN EACH OF US WHO NEVER CEASES TO EXPRESS UNCONDITIONAL LOVE FOR OURSELVES AND OTHERS, AND CONSTANTLY REMINDS US THAT ALL THERE IS IS **NOW**.

INTRODUCTION

What would your life look like if you had plenty of time?

How often do you find yourself in such a hurry that you feel like you don't have time to do all you want to; to see people you love, or to take care of yourself?

Raising young children I remember feeling like there weren't enough hours in a day. Managing a business always left me closing out the day wishing I could check a few more items off my list. I have even found myself running from a yoga class to a massage appointment! Certainly all the gadgets that allow us to be in communication every waking hour aren't giving us the experience of more time. So *maybe* it's not managing the circumstances of our lives that will free us from the time crunch. What if it's all about the context of our life: what our life is for; what our hours are for? Why are those things on your to-do list? What makes them a priority?

Plenty Of Time is a new way of looking at your life, a new way of composing your day – moment by moment. Rather than organizing your day around what you *have* to *do*, you will create your day using *who* you want to *be* as your guiding star. When you utilize this book as your system, you will have the tools to sort through the "to-dos" on your list and create them instead as *opportunities* for who you get to be.

We have chosen six divine qualities to focus on and we welcome you to add any that inspire you. Simply take your to-do list and choose what quality you are going to be practicing while accomplishing that task. For example, a dental appointment might be an opportunity to practice Being Loving & Accepting. Or a meeting with a potential investor might be an opportunity to practice Being Worthy.
I have filled out a practice page so you can get the idea. Fill it out any way you want. Each page is divided in half, so you can create your own time slots (AM/PM, etc.). Use your imagination – this is your tool to support you in creating a life you love!

Here is what I promise you: a completely new experience of your day to day life – the freedom to create your life as an expression that inspires and brings out the best in you. Remember this is a practice, so keep it up. Who do you get to be in re-creating your life?
It is my sincerest hope that you will create Being Grateful, and that you will see there really is Plenty Of Time.

Love,
Terces

Acknowledgment:

I want to thank, from the bottom of my heart, Jon Marro. He listened so intently when I shared with him my vision for this book. I so wanted people to know about the possibility of re-creating their lives in a way that empowers them and what they are up to. Jon took my idea and created a masterpiece. He is an artist and a visionary and working with him became a practice in Being Inspired.

Thank you Jon for creating *Plenty of Time* as a reality.

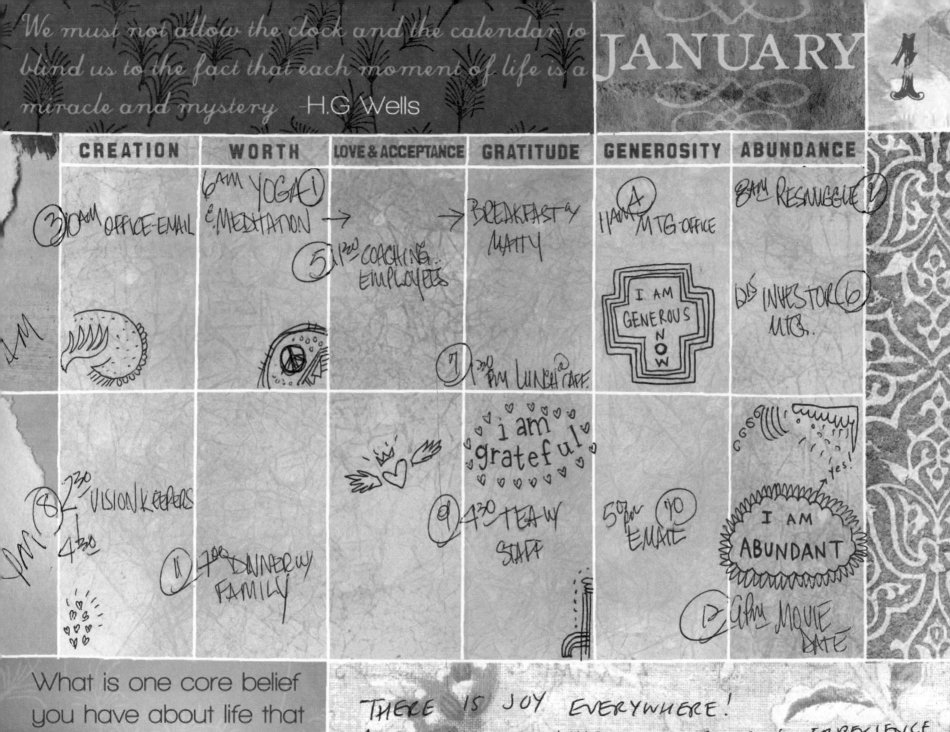

JANUARY 1

> We must not allow the clock and the calendar to blind us to the fact that each moment of life is a miracle and mystery —H.G Wells

CREATION	WORTH	LOVE & ACCEPTANCE	GRATITUDE	GENEROSITY	ABUNDANCE
③ 10AM OFFICE-EMAIL	6AM YOGA ① & MEDITATION →	⑤ 1:30 COACHING.. EMPLOYEES	→ BREAKFAST w MATTY	11AM ④ MTG·OFFICE	8AM RESNUGGLE ②
			⑦ 1:30PM LUNCH CAFE	I AM GENEROUS NOW	1:45 INVESTOR ⑥ MTG.
2:30 ⑧ VISION KEEPERS 4:30	⑪ 7:00 DINNER w FAMILY		i am grateful ⑨ 4:30 TEA w STAFF	5:00 for ⑩ EMATE	I AM ABUNDANT ⑫ 6PM MOVIE DATE

What is one core belief you have about life that you love?

THERE IS JOY EVERYWHERE!
AND I FEEL LIKE EVERYTHING I EXPERIENCE IS A GIFT FROM THE UNIVERSE JUST FOR ME!

TIME IS A FLOWING RIVER.

HAPPY THOSE WHO ALLOW THEMSELVES

TO BE CARRIED, UNRESISTING,

WITH THE CURRENT.

THEY FLOAT

THROUGH EASY DAYS.

THEY LIVE,

UNQUESTIONING, IN THE MOMENT.

— Christopher Morley

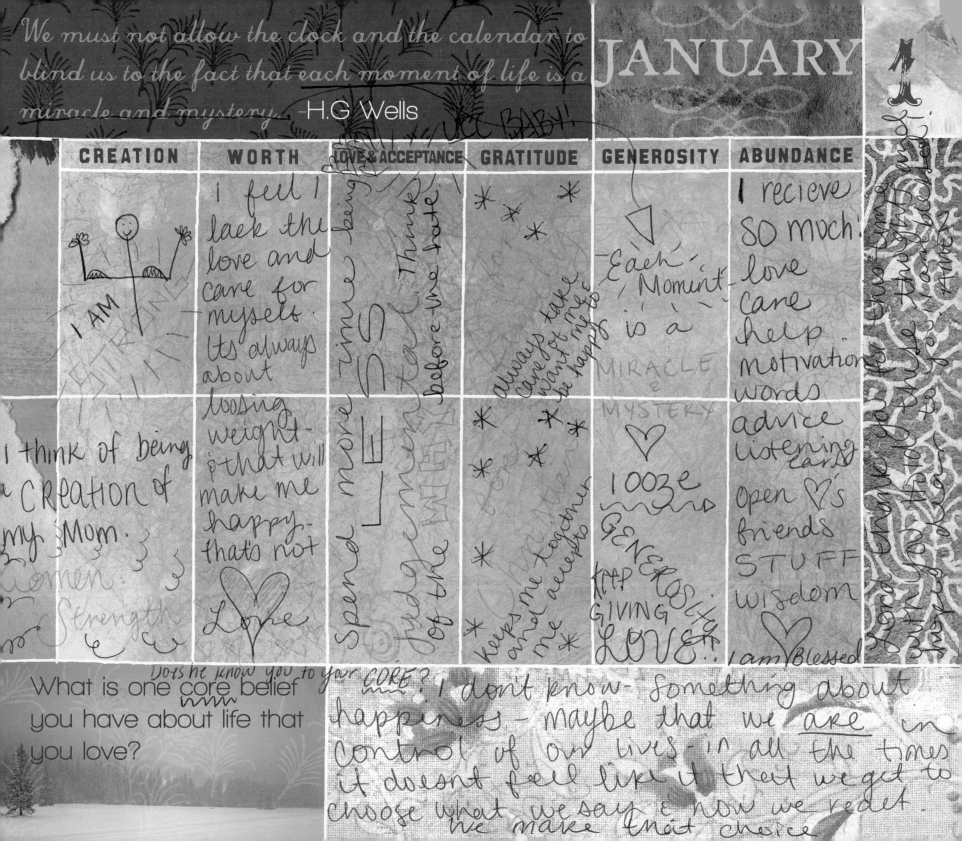

We must not allow the clock and the calendar to blind us to the fact that each moment of life is a miracle and mystery. —H.G Wells

YOU BABY!

JANUARY 1

CREATION	WORTH	LOVE & ACCEPTANCE	GRATITUDE	GENEROSITY	ABUNDANCE
I AM	I feel I lack the love and care for myself. Its always about loosing weight—& that will make me happy. that's not Love	Spend more time being LESS judgemental. Think before we hate of the	✱ ✱ ✱ ✱ ✱ ✱ ✱ always take care of me— want me to be happy keeps me together and accepts me	Each Moment is a MIRACLE & MYSTERY ♡ 100% GENEROSITY keep GIVING LOVE	I recieve SO much: love care help motivation words advice listening cards open ♡'s friends STUFF wisdom ♡ I am Blessed
I think of being a CREATION of my Mom. women Strength					

What is one core belief you have about life that you love?

Does he know you to your CORE?

I don't know—something about happiness—maybe that we are in control of our lives—in all the times it doesn't feel like it that we get to choose what we say & how we react. we make that choice

When you realize nothing is lacking, the whole world belongs to you.

-Lao Tzu

Recycling
goodwill
dishes
Wax
groceries
office
sms
TARGET

CREATION	WORTH	LOVE & ACCEPTANCE	GRATITUDE	GENEROSITY	ABUNDANCE
Recycling, before 3 take care of this	CALL THEM WAX ✓ Self WORTH 3:15	SMS I have loving friends			The Office Get rid of STUFF
dishes — CREATE a livable space!			GROCERIES -greatful we can- TARGET	GOODWILL be generous!	

What are five material things you have an abundance of now?

Shoes
Clothes
Memory stuff
BODY CARE STUFF
COATS

May you live all the days of your life.

—Jonathan Swift

JANUARY 3

CREATION	WORTH	LOVE & ACCEPTANCE	GRATITUDE	GENEROSITY	ABUNDANCE

How has life prepared you for now?

To him that has, more shall be given, but from him that has not, the little he has shall be taken away. -Matthew 13:11-13

JANUARY

4

CREATION	WORTH	LOVE & ACCEPTANCE	GRATITUDE	GENEROSITY	ABUNDANCE

If money were no consideration, what would your life be for?

One cannot see God as long as one feels, "I am the doer".

Rama Krishna

JANUARY 5

CREATION	WORTH	LOVE & ACCEPTANCE	GRATITUDE	GENEROSITY	ABUNDANCE

What is sacred about food?

An Abundance mentality springs from internal security, not from external rankings, comparisons, opinions, possessions, or associations.

—Stephen R. Covey

JANUARY 6

CREATION	WORTH	LOVE & ACCEPTANCE	GRATITUDE	GENEROSITY	ABUNDANCE

Write down three things that support your existence.

Every thought you have contributes to truth or illusion. It either extends the truth or multiplies illusions.

-A Course In Miracles

JANUARY 7

CREATION	WORTH	LOVE & ACCEPTANCE	GRATITUDE	GENEROSITY	ABUNDANCE

What is a childlike quality you would like to experience more of?

How few our real wants, and how vast our imaginary ones!

-John Casper Lavater

JANUARY 8

CREATION	WORTH	LOVE & ACCEPTANCE	GRATITUDE	GENEROSITY	ABUNDANCE

Who are three people that have contributed to you and your life?

Abundance is knowing that everything you need has already been supplied.

-Shanti Das

JANUARY 9

CREATION	WORTH	LOVE & ACCEPTANCE	GRATITUDE	GENEROSITY	ABUNDANCE

Can you consider that your life is steeped in evidence of always being provided for?

He is well paid that is well satisfied.

-William Shakespeare

JANUARY 10

CREATION	WORTH	LOVE & ACCEPTANCE	GRATITUDE	GENEROSITY	ABUNDANCE

What is your BIGGEST unfulfilled desire in the material world?

If we are not responsible for the thoughts that pass our doors, we are at least responsible for those we admit and entertain.

—Charles B. Newcomb

CREATION	WORTH	LOVE & ACCEPTANCE	GRATITUDE	GENEROSITY	ABUNDANCE

With whom could you be more generous?

It is not because things are difficult that we do not dare; it is because we do not dare that things are difficult.
—Seneca

JANUARY 12

CREATION	WORTH	LOVE & ACCEPTANCE	GRATITUDE	GENEROSITY	ABUNDANCE

What word do you use for God, Spirit, etc.?

One of the ego's favorite paths of resistance is to fill you with doubt.

-Ram Dass

JANUARY 13

CREATION	WORTH	LOVE & ACCEPTANCE	GRATITUDE	GENEROSITY	ABUNDANCE

Say out loud three times:
I love myself and others
as ___(Spirit Word)___.

True affluence is not needing anything.

-Gary Snyder

JANUARY 14

CREATION	WORTH	LOVE & ACCEPTANCE	GRATITUDE	GENEROSITY	ABUNDANCE

What don't you consciously want for everyone, that perhaps you want for yourself?

We should take care not to make the intellect our God.

-Albert Einstein

CREATION	WORTH	LOVE & ACCEPTANCE	GRATITUDE	GENEROSITY	ABUNDANCE

Who do you have no compassion for?

Abundance can be had simply by consciously receiving what has already been given.

-Sufi saying

JANUARY 16

CREATION	WORTH	LOVE & ACCEPTANCE	GRATITUDE	GENEROSITY	ABUNDANCE

Name something you frequently say you don't have enough of.

Truth has no special time of its own.
Its hour is now—always.
—Albert Schweitzer

JANUARY 17

CREATION	WORTH	LOVE & ACCEPTANCE	GRATITUDE	GENEROSITY	ABUNDANCE
			WORK I am happy there is work this week & I have a regular schedule!		
Chicken Pesto tonight!	gym —love yourself—			Write Shinya a thank you letter! Work on Ref. letter Write Orangtua a letter	Clean!

Have you ever chosen happiness regardless of the circumstances?

Yes—but to think of the time—I dont know I think it is always easier when others are going through it with me, then it's easier to do it. When it comes to just me I tend to play a victim. But thats whats great about Christian, he can play my + person for me and let me have a pity party. I think it's a balance

Fear not, little flock, for it is your Father's good pleasure to give you the kingdom.

-Luke 12:32

JANUARY 18

CREATION	WORTH	LOVE & ACCEPTANCE	GRATITUDE	GENEROSITY	ABUNDANCE

What are you really afraid of?

Reality is merely an illusion, albeit a very persistent one.

—Albert Einstein

JANUARY 19

CREATION	WORTH	LOVE & ACCEPTANCE	GRATITUDE	GENEROSITY	ABUNDANCE

What is the gift of being really present?

Faith begins as an experiment
and ends as an experience.
—W. R. Inge

JANUARY 20

CREATION	WORTH	LOVE & ACCEPTANCE	GRATITUDE	GENEROSITY	ABUNDANCE

If you were to make a request of a friend for money, whom would you ask?

JANUARY 21

CREATION	WORTH	LOVE & ACCEPTANCE	GRATITUDE	GENEROSITY	ABUNDANCE

Where does life exceed your expectations?

You have to believe in Gods
to see them.

-Hopi saying

JANUARY 22

CREATION	WORTH	LOVE & ACCEPTANCE	GRATITUDE	GENEROSITY	ABUNDANCE

Where don't you trust
Spirit?

The currents of Universal Being circulate through me; I am part and parcel of God.
—Ralph Waldo Emerson

JANUARY 23

CREATION	WORTH	LOVE & ACCEPTANCE	GRATITUDE	GENEROSITY	ABUNDANCE

Who is really generous with you?

The only thing you have to remember is how fortunate you are.

-Sri Sri Ravi Shankar

JANUARY 24

CREATION	WORTH	LOVE & ACCEPTANCE	GRATITUDE	GENEROSITY	ABUNDANCE

Can you consider money is just another opportunity to be present to "Spirit"?

All that we are is the result of what we have thought. The mind is everything. What we think we become. —Buddha

JANUARY 25

CREATION	WORTH	LOVE & ACCEPTANCE	GRATITUDE	GENEROSITY	ABUNDANCE

Who inspires you?

Better is a handful with quietness than both hands full together with toil and grasping for the wind. —Ecclesiastes 4:6

JANUARY 26

CREATION	WORTH	LOVE & ACCEPTANCE	GRATITUDE	GENEROSITY	ABUNDANCE

Say out loud three times:
I am open to receiving:
___(Spirit Word)___ .

Without the assistance of the Divine Being...I cannot succeed. With that assistance, I cannot fail. -Abraham Lincoln

JANUARY 27

CREATION	WORTH	LOVE & ACCEPTANCE	GRATITUDE	GENEROSITY	ABUNDANCE

What is your greatest asset?

If you want to be given everything, give up everything.

—Lao Tzu

JANUARY

28

CREATION	WORTH	LOVE & ACCEPTANCE	GRATITUDE	GENEROSITY	ABUNDANCE

When it comes to money, what do you frequently worry about?

Let one therefore keep the mind pure, for what a man thinks, that he becomes.

-The Upanishads

JANUARY 29

CREATION	WORTH	LOVE & ACCEPTANCE	GRATITUDE	GENEROSITY	ABUNDANCE

Where could you be more flexible?

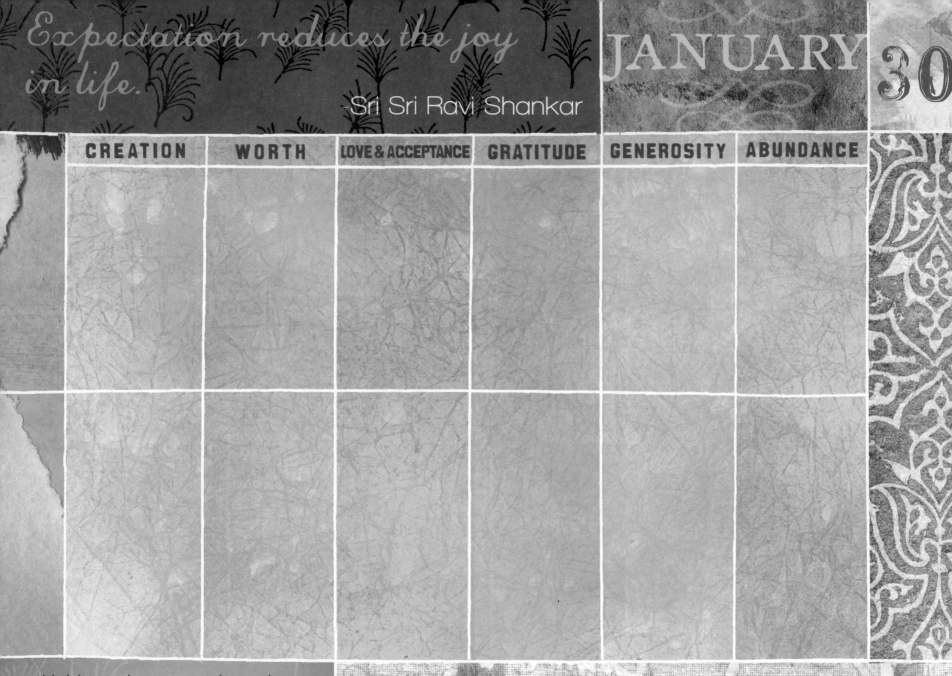

Expectation reduces the joy in life.

—Sri Sri Ravi Shankar

JANUARY 30

CREATION	WORTH	LOVE & ACCEPTANCE	GRATITUDE	GENEROSITY	ABUNDANCE

Write about a time in your life when you were provided for in a way that you couldn't predict.

Not by which the eye sees but by which the eye can see.
-The Upanishads

JANUARY 31

CREATION	WORTH	LOVE & ACCEPTANCE	GRATITUDE	GENEROSITY	ABUNDANCE

When do you feel most alive?

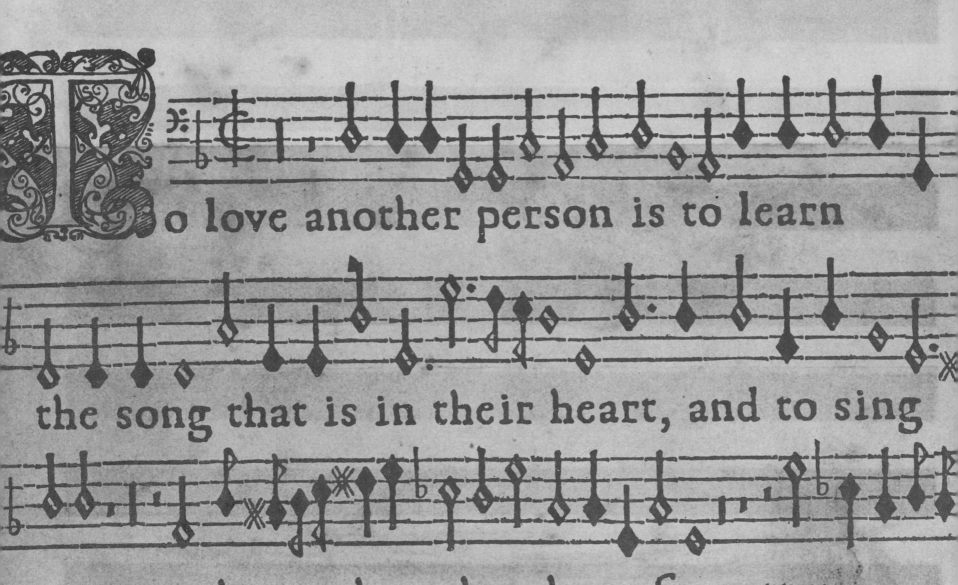

o love another person is to learn

the song that is in their heart, and to sing

it to them when they have forgotten.

-THOMAS CHANDLER

EVERYONE IS QUOTABLE.

FEBRUARY 1

+ amanda sayre caskey

CREATION	WORTH	LOVE & ACCEPTANCE	GRATITUDE	GENEROSITY	ABUNDANCE

WHO DO YOU SERVE?

BY LETTING GO IT ALL GETS DONE. THE
WORLD IS WON BY THOSE WHO LET IT GO.
BUT WHEN YOU TRY AND TRY, THE WORLD
IS BEYOND WINNING.

+ lao tzu

FEBRUARY 2

CREATION	WORTH	LOVE & ACCEPTANCE	GRATITUDE	GENEROSITY	ABUNDANCE

WRITE DOWN ONE
THING YOU DO NOT
WANT TO ADMIT
ABOUT YOUR
FINANCES

YOU ARE WHAT YOU ARE BY
WHAT YOU BELIEVE.

• oprah winfrey

FEBRUARY 3

CREATION	WORTH	LOVE & ACCEPTANCE	GRATITUDE	GENEROSITY	ABUNDANCE

TO WHOM CAN YOU GIVE THANKS?

IN ORDER TO HAVE SOMETHING, YOU MUST FIRST BE SOMETHING.

◆ goethe

FEBRUARY 4

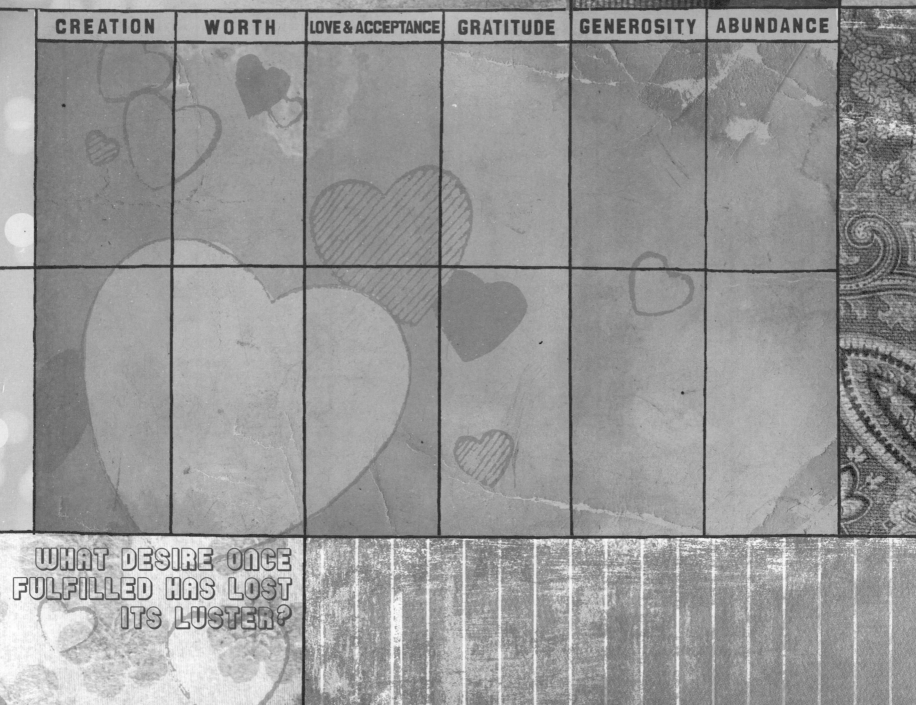

CREATION	WORTH	LOVE & ACCEPTANCE	GRATITUDE	GENEROSITY	ABUNDANCE

WHAT DESIRE ONCE FULFILLED HAS LOST ITS LUSTER?

THE LANGUAGE OF TRUTH IS UNADORNED AND SIMPLE.

+ marcellinus ammianus

FEBRUARY 5

CREATION	WORTH	LOVE & ACCEPTANCE	GRATITUDE	GENEROSITY	ABUNDANCE

WHEN HAS THE UNKNOWN BEEN YOUR TEACHER?

DO NOT WORRY ABOUT TOMORROW
FOR TOMORROW WILL WORRY ABOUT
ITS OWN THINGS.

+ matthew 6:34

FEBRUARY 6

CREATION	WORTH	LOVE & ACCEPTANCE	GRATITUDE	GENEROSITY	ABUNDANCE

WHAT IS SOMETHING YOU ARE HOLDING ON TO THAT YOU COULD GIVE AWAY?

THOUGH WE TRAVEL THE WORLD
TO FIND THE BEAUTIFUL, WE MUST
CARRY IT WITH US OR WE FIND IT NOT.
+ ralph waldo emerson

FEBRUARY 7

CREATION	WORTH	LOVE & ACCEPTANCE	GRATITUDE	GENEROSITY	ABUNDANCE

WHAT DO YOU REALLY HAVE FAITH IN?

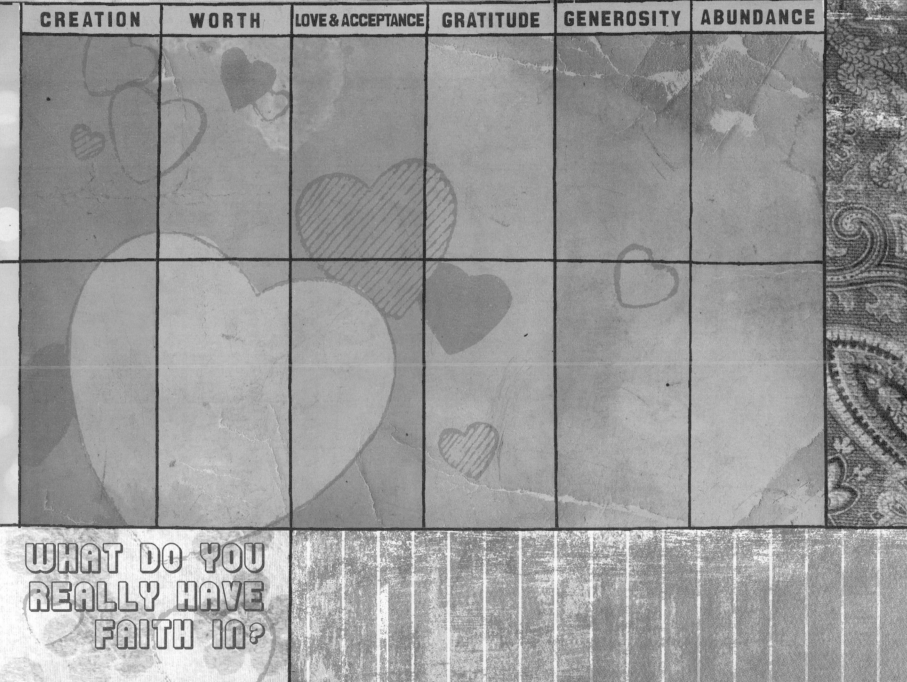

THE OUTER SITUATION IS ALWAYS A
REFLECTION OF THE COLLECTIVE INNER
SITUATION.

+ peace pilgrim

FEBRUARY 8

CREATION	WORTH	LOVE & ACCEPTANCE	GRATITUDE	GENEROSITY	ABUNDANCE

WHAT IS A GENEROUS
BELIEF YOU COULD
PUT YOUR ATTENTION
ON NOW?

IN EVERYTHING DO TO OTHERS AS YOU WOULD HAVE THEM DO TO YOU, FOR THIS IS THE LAW OF THE PROPHETS.
+ matthew 7:11-13

FEBRUARY 9

CREATION	WORTH	LOVE & ACCEPTANCE	GRATITUDE	GENEROSITY	ABUNDANCE

WHAT IS YOUR BIGGEST SURPRISE IN LIFE?

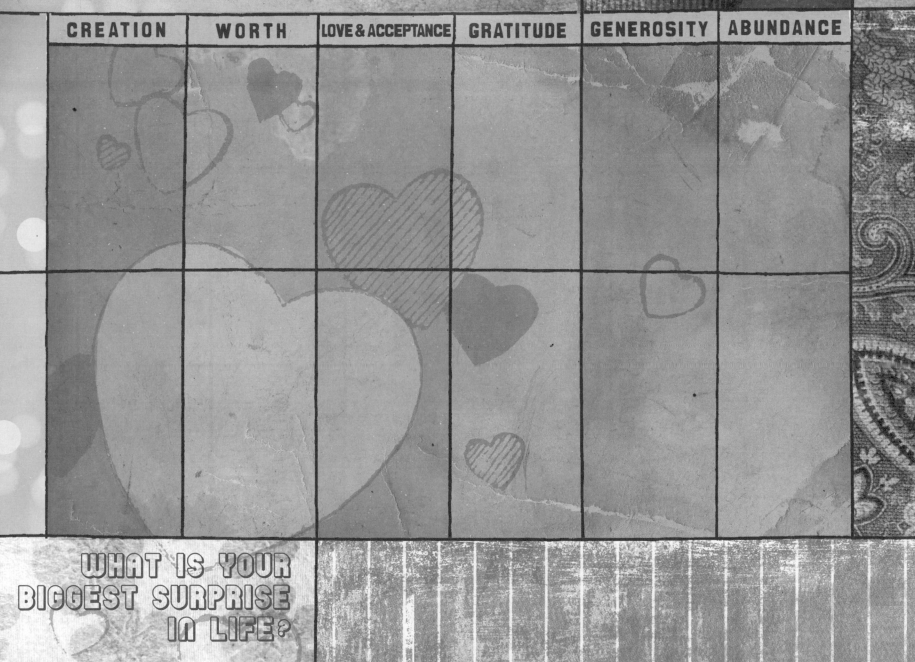

A MAN IS RICH IN PROPORTION TO THE NUMBER OF THINGS HE CAN LET ALONE.

✦ henry david thoreau

FEBRUARY 10

CREATION	WORTH	LOVE & ACCEPTANCE	GRATITUDE	GENEROSITY	ABUNDANCE

UNDER WHAT CIRCUMSTANCES DO YOU EXPERIENCE YOURSELF AS BEING STINGY?

NOTHING IS GOOD OR BAD, BUT THINKING MAKES IT SO.

+ william shakespeare

FEBRUARY 11

CREATION	WORTH	LOVE & ACCEPTANCE	GRATITUDE	GENEROSITY	ABUNDANCE

WHEN IS LESS MORE?

MY RICHES CONSIST NOT IN THE EXTENT
OF MY POSSESSIONS, BUT IN THE
FEWNESS OF MY WANTS.

j brotherton

CREATION	WORTH	LOVE & ACCEPTANCE	GRATITUDE	GENEROSITY	ABUNDANCE

WHAT IS SOMETHING
THAT LEAVES YOU
FEELING A SENSE OF
SCARCITY OR LACK?

ONE'S OWN THOUGHT IS ONE'S WORLD.
WHAT A PERSON THINKS HE BECOMES -
THAT IS THE ETERNAL MYSTERY.

+ the upanishads

FEBRUARY 13

CREATION	WORTH	LOVE & ACCEPTANCE	GRATITUDE	GENEROSITY	ABUNDANCE

SAY OUT LOUD THREE TIMES:

I HONOR AND VALUE MYSELF.

BEING HUMAN MEANS THROWING YOUR WHOLE
LIFE ON THE SCALES OF DESTINY WHEN NEED
BE, ALL THE WHILE REJOICING IN EVERY
SUNNY DAY AND EVERY BEAUTIFUL CLOUD.

◆ rosa luxemburg

FEBRUARY 14

CREATION	WORTH	LOVE & ACCEPTANCE	GRATITUDE	GENEROSITY	ABUNDANCE

IDENTIFY A FINANCIAL
SITUATION IN YOUR
LIFE THAT YOU DO NOT
LIKE OR WISH WERE
DIFFERENT.

WHAT CONCERNS ME IS NOT THE WAY THINGS ARE BUT RATHER THE WAY PEOPLE THINK THINGS ARE. + epictetus

FEBRUARY 15

CREATION	WORTH	LOVE & ACCEPTANCE	GRATITUDE	GENEROSITY	ABUNDANCE

WHAT DO YOUR FRIENDS LOVE ABOUT YOU?

THERE IS A TREASURY OF JOY
WITHIN YOU; WHY DO YOU KEEP
BEGGING DOOR TO DOOR?

+ sufi saying

FEBRUARY 16

CREATION	WORTH	LOVE & ACCEPTANCE	GRATITUDE	GENEROSITY	ABUNDANCE

ASK THE NEXT
PERSON YOU SEE
FOR A DOLLAR.

OUR TRUE ACQUISITIONS LIE ONLY IN OUR CHARITIES; WE GAIN ONLY AS WE GIVE.

+ william simms

FEBRUARY 17

CREATION	WORTH	LOVE & ACCEPTANCE	GRATITUDE	GENEROSITY	ABUNDANCE

IN WHOSE PRESENCE ARE YOU MOST ALIVE?

AT THAT DAY YOU WILL KNOW
THAT I AM IN MY FATHER AND
YOU IN ME AND I IN YOU。
+john 14:20

FEBRUARY 18

CREATION	WORTH	LOVE & ACCEPTANCE	GRATITUDE	GENEROSITY	ABUNDANCE

WHAT DO YOU
LOVE ABOUT YOUR
BODY?

GIVING IS THE SECRET OF ABUNDANCE.

+ sivananda

FEBRUARY 19

CREATION	WORTH	LOVE & ACCEPTANCE	GRATITUDE	GENEROSITY	ABUNDANCE

HOW DO YOU NOURISH YOURSELF?

OUR ENTIRE LIFE...CONSISTS ULTIMATELY IN ACCEPTING OURSELVES AS WE ARE.

✦ jean anouilh

FEBRUARY 20

CREATION	WORTH	LOVE & ACCEPTANCE	GRATITUDE	GENEROSITY	ABUNDANCE

IDENTIFY SOME CIRCUMSTANCE IN YOUR LIFE THAT YOU REGRET OR BLAME YOURSELF FOR.

THERE ARE NO OTHERS.

✦ ramana maharishi

FEBRUARY 21

CREATION	WORTH	LOVE & ACCEPTANCE	GRATITUDE	GENEROSITY	ABUNDANCE

WHEN DO YOU EXPERIENCE THE ECSTATIC?

YOU MUST SEE GOD INSIDE OF YOU BEFORE YOU RECOGNIZE IT IN ANOTHER. +ma jaya sati bhagavati

FEBRUARY 22

CREATION	WORTH	LOVE & ACCEPTANCE	GRATITUDE	GENEROSITY	ABUNDANCE

GIVE THE NEXT PERSON YOU SEE A DOLLAR.

GOD LOVETH A CHEERFUL GIVER.

FEBRUARY 23

CREATION	WORTH	LOVE & ACCEPTANCE	GRATITUDE	GENEROSITY	ABUNDANCE

ARE YOU FULFILLED?

THIS ABOVE ALL: TO THINE OWN SELF
BE TRUE; AND IT MUST FOLLOW, AS THE
NIGHT THE DAY, THOU CANST NOT THEN
BE FALSE TO ANY MAN. + william shakespeare

FEBRUARY 24

CREATION	WORTH	LOVE & ACCEPTANCE	GRATITUDE	GENEROSITY	ABUNDANCE

WHOM HAVE YOU MADE
A FINANCIAL PROMISE
TO, OR WHO HAS MADE
A FINANCIAL PROMISE
TO YOU, THAT HAS NOT
BEEN KEPT?

A GENEROUS HEART IS A HAPPY HEART.

• ida s• taylor

FEBRUARY 25

CREATION	WORTH	LOVE & ACCEPTANCE	GRATITUDE	GENEROSITY	ABUNDANCE

ARE YOU A GOLD MEDALIST IN RECEIVING?

THE WORLD YOU SEE WHEN YOU ARE
GIVING LOVE IS NOT THE SAME WORLD
YOU SEE WHEN YOU ARE DEMANDING IT.

+ paul ferrini

FEBRUARY 26

CREATION	WORTH	LOVE & ACCEPTANCE	GRATITUDE	GENEROSITY	ABUNDANCE

SAY OUT LOUD
THREE TIMES:

I LOVE RELEASING

UNHAPPINESS IS THE HUNGER
TO GET. HAPPINESS IS THE
HUNGER TO GIVE.
✦ william george jordan

FEBRUARY 27

CREATION	WORTH	LOVE & ACCEPTANCE	GRATITUDE	GENEROSITY	ABUNDANCE

IS YOUR LIFE
ALIGNED WITH
YOUR HIGHEST
INTENTION?

IF YOU MAKE FRIENDS WITH YOURSELF YOU WILL NEVER BE ALONE.

• maxwell maltz

FEBRUARY 28

CREATION	WORTH	LOVE & ACCEPTANCE	GRATITUDE	GENEROSITY	ABUNDANCE

WHAT IS SOMETHING YOU OWN RIGHT NOW THAT YOU ARE NOT RELISHING?

WE CANNOT LIVE ONLY FOR OURSELVES.
A THOUSAND FIBERS CONNECT US WITH
OUR FELLOW MEN.

+ herman melville

FEBRUARY 29

CREATION	WORTH	LOVE & ACCEPTANCE	GRATITUDE	GENEROSITY	ABUNDANCE

ARE YOU EVER
OVERWHELMED BY
BEAUTY?

TREES BEND LOW WITH RIPENED FRUIT,
CLOUDS HANG DOWN WITH GENTLE
RAIN, NOBLE MEN BOW GRACIOUSLY,
THIS IS THE WAY OF GENEROUS THINGS.

Bhartrihari

march 1

CREATION	WORTH	LOVE & ACCEPTANCE	GRATITUDE	GENEROSITY	ABUNDANCE

What have you overcome?

I HAVE AN EVERYDAY RELIGION THAT WORKS FOR ME: LOVE YOURSELF FIRST AND EVERYTHING ELSE FALLS IN PLACE.

Lucille Ball

march 2

CREATION	WORTH	LOVE & ACCEPTANCE	GRATITUDE	GENEROSITY	ABUNDANCE

What limits your experience of being abundant?

GOD DIVIDED MAN INTO MEN THAT
THEY MIGHT HELP EACH OTHER.

Seneca

march 3

CREATION	WORTH	LOVE & ACCEPTANCE	GRATITUDE	GENEROSITY	ABUNDANCE

What ingredient would you add to your life?

A PERSON IS IN HELL WHO HAS LOST HIS SELF ESTEEM.

Robert Schuller

march 4

CREATION	WORTH	LOVE & ACCEPTANCE	GRATITUDE	GENEROSITY	ABUNDANCE

Who in your life are you grateful for right now?

WHEN I DON'T KNOW MYSELF I SERVE YOU. WHEN I KNOW MYSELF I AM YOU.

Werner Erhard

march 5

CREATION	WORTH	LOVE & ACCEPTANCE	GRATITUDE	GENEROSITY	ABUNDANCE

Where has your desire for comfort and security cost you some aliveness?

I EXIST AS I AM, THAT IS ENOUGH. IF NO OTHER IN THE WORLD BE AWARE, I SIT CONTENT. AND IF EACH AND ALL BE AWARE, I SIT CONTENT. *Walt Whitman*

march 6

CREATION	WORTH	LOVE & ACCEPTANCE	GRATITUDE	GENEROSITY	ABUNDANCE

What is something you would like to receive right now?

THE WHOLE WORTH OF A
BENEVOLENT DEED LIES IN THE
LOVE THAT INSPIRES IT.

The Talmud

m a r c h 7

CREATION	WORTH	LOVE & ACCEPTANCE	GRATITUDE	GENEROSITY	ABUNDANCE

With whom have you broken your word?

RESOLVE TO BE THYSELF. HE WHO FINDS HIMSELF LOSES HIS MISERY.

Matthew Arnold

march 8

CREATION	WORTH	LOVE & ACCEPTANCE	GRATITUDE	GENEROSITY	ABUNDANCE

Can you see that without someone's receiving, there is no opportunity to give?

MY RELIGION IS KINDNESS.

Dalai Lama

march 9

CREATION	WORTH	LOVE & ACCEPTANCE	GRATITUDE	GENEROSITY	ABUNDANCE

What do you love about your mother?

ABOVE ALL THINGS, REVERE YOURSELF.

Pythagoras

march 10

CREATION	WORTH	LOVE & ACCEPTANCE	GRATITUDE	GENEROSITY	ABUNDANCE

What could you do to make someone's day today?

MOST OF THE SHADOWS OF THIS LIFE
ARE CAUSED BY STANDING IN OUR
OWN SUNSHINE.

Ralph Waldo Emerson

march 11

CREATION	WORTH	LOVE & ACCEPTANCE	GRATITUDE	GENEROSITY	ABUNDANCE

For what can you thank the plant kingdom?

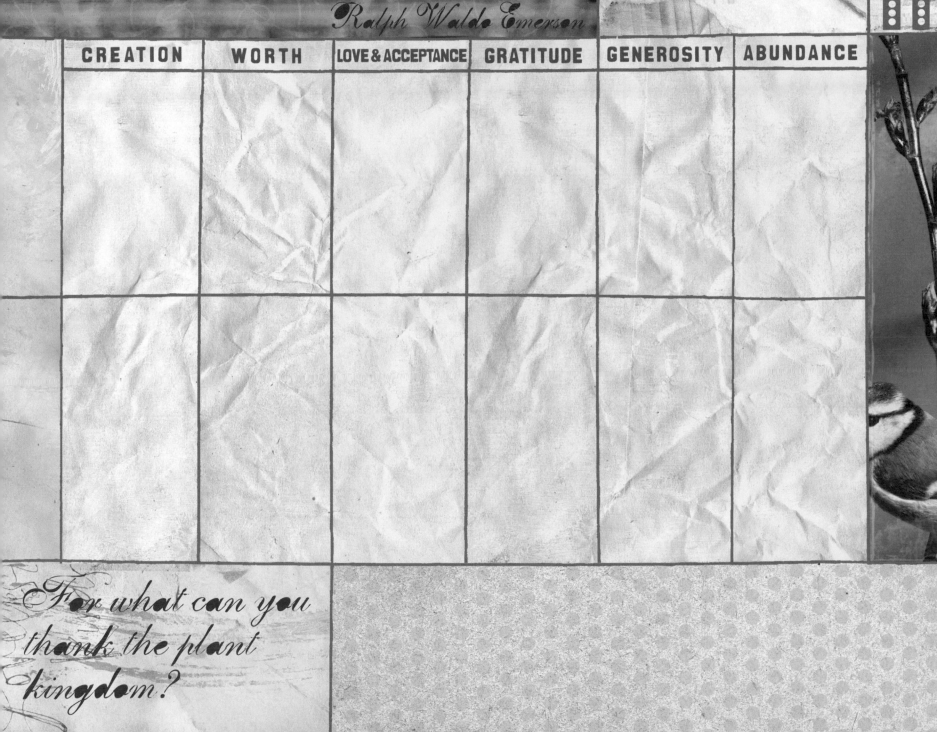

I SAID, YE ARE GODS AND ALL OF YOU ARE CHILDREN OF THE MOST HIGH.

Psalms 82:6

march 12

CREATION	WORTH	LOVE & ACCEPTANCE	GRATITUDE	GENEROSITY	ABUNDANCE

What is one thing about yourself you are grateful for?

THE VERY ACT OF GIVING, WITH ITS APPARENT LOSS, TENDS TO THROW US UPON SPIRIT AND MAKE US DEPEND UPON GOD FOR SUPPLY.

Henry T. Hambill

march 13

CREATION	WORTH	LOVE & ACCEPTANCE	GRATITUDE	GENEROSITY	ABUNDANCE

Say out loud three times:
I love and appreciate my life now.

YOU ARE GODS.

John 10:34

march 14

CREATION	WORTH	LOVE & ACCEPTANCE	GRATITUDE	GENEROSITY	ABUNDANCE

How can you contribute to the world you want to live in?.

BLESSED ARE THOSE WHO GIVE WITHOUT REMEMBERING AND TAKE WITHOUT FORGETTING.

Melvin Schleeds

march 15

CREATION	WORTH	LOVE & ACCEPTANCE	GRATITUDE	GENEROSITY	ABUNDANCE

In what way has the universe dealt you a royal flush?

IF GOD HAD WANTED ME OTHERWISE HE WOULD HAVE CREATED ME OTHERWISE.

Johann Von Goethe

march 16

CREATION	WORTH	LOVE & ACCEPTANCE	GRATITUDE	GENEROSITY	ABUNDANCE

List three things you can praise.

A COVETOUS MAN IS ALWAYS POOR.

Claudian

march 17

CREATION	WORTH	LOVE & ACCEPTANCE	GRATITUDE	GENEROSITY	ABUNDANCE

Where do you invest your attention?

YOU ARE SITTING ON THE EARTH AND YOU REALIZE
THAT THIS EARTH DESERVES YOU AND YOU DESERVE
THIS EARTH. YOU ARE THERE - FULLY, PERSONALLY,
GENUINELY.

Chogyum Trungpa

march 18

CREATION	WORTH	LOVE & ACCEPTANCE	GRATITUDE	GENEROSITY	ABUNDANCE

Where could you be more generous with yourself?

WE EMPTY OURSELVES TO BE
FILLED WITH GOD. EVEN GOD
CANNOT FILL WHAT IS FULL.
Mother Teresa

march
23

CREATION	WORTH	LOVE & ACCEPTANCE	GRATITUDE	GENEROSITY	ABUNDANCE

What is true about you?

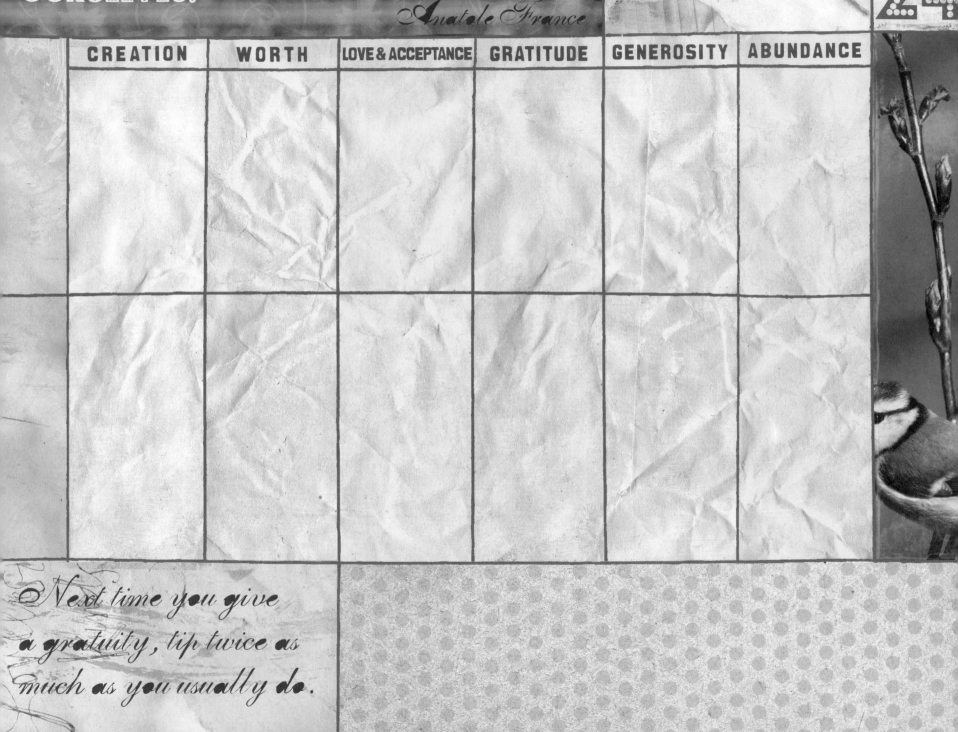

NO MATTER HOW MUCH WE SEEK,
WE NEVER FIND ANYTHING BUT
OURSELVES.

Anatole France

march 24

CREATION	WORTH	LOVE & ACCEPTANCE	GRATITUDE	GENEROSITY	ABUNDANCE

*Next time you give
a gratuity, tip twice as
much as you usually do.*

KINDNESS COSTS NOTHING.

Irish Proverb

march 25

CREATION	WORTH	LOVE & ACCEPTANCE	GRATITUDE	GENEROSITY	ABUNDANCE

For whom or what can you kneel and kiss the ground?

WHERE DO YOU GO IN SEARCH OF GOD?
HE IS WITH YOU.

Kabir

march 26

CREATION	WORTH	LOVE & ACCEPTANCE	GRATITUDE	GENEROSITY	ABUNDANCE

Say out loud three times:
I am now present to the magnificence of my life!

A WISE MAN DOES NOT LAY UP HIS TREASURES. THE MORE HE GIVES TO OTHERS THE MORE HE HAS.

Lao Tzu

march 27

CREATION	WORTH	LOVE & ACCEPTANCE	GRATITUDE	GENEROSITY	ABUNDANCE

Do you have wants or do your wants have you?

THE DESIRE AND PURSUIT OF
THE WHOLE IS CALLED LOVE.

Plato

march 28

CREATION	WORTH	LOVE & ACCEPTANCE	GRATITUDE	GENEROSITY	ABUNDANCE

Whom in your life are you currently resenting or making wrong?

WE ARE MADE KIND BY BEING KIND.

Eric Hoffer

CREATION	WORTH	LOVE & ACCEPTANCE	GRATITUDE	GENEROSITY	ABUNDANCE

Praise some aspect of nature that supports your existence.

IT IS DIFFICULT TO MAKE A MAN MISERABLE WHILE HE
FEELS HE IS WORTHY OF HIMSELF AND CLAIMS
KINDRED TO THE GREAT GOD WHO MADE HIM.

Abraham Lincoln

m a r c h 30

CREATION	WORTH	LOVE & ACCEPTANCE	GRATITUDE	GENEROSITY	ABUNDANCE

How could you contribute to making someone else's dream come true?

SUPPLY IS NOT GETTING, SUPPLY IS GIVING. THE BREAD THAT YOU CAST UPON THE WATER IS THE BREAD THAT COMES BACK TO YOU.

Joel Goldstein

march 31

CREATION	WORTH	LOVE & ACCEPTANCE	GRATITUDE	GENEROSITY	ABUNDANCE

Ask yourself often: what would love do now?

THE TREE

WHICH MOVES SOME

TO TEARS OF JOY

IS IN THE EYES OF OTHERS

A GREEN THING

WHICH STANDS IN THE WAY

AS A MAN IS

SO HE SEES

-BLAKE-

Happiness and love are just a choice away.

-LEO BUSCAGLIA

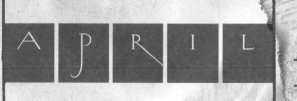

CREATION	WORTH	LOVE & ACCEPTANCE	GRATITUDE	GENEROSITY	ABUNDANCE

What is your biggest commitment?

A man cannot be comfortable
without his own approval.

-MARK TWAIN

APRIL 2

CREATION	WORTH	LOVE & ACCEPTANCE	GRATITUDE	GENEROSITY	ABUNDANCE

Consider that Spirit is always
expressing an abundance of whatever
you have your attention on.

What wisdom can you find that is greater than kindness?

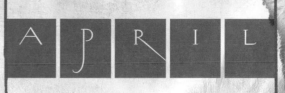

APRIL 3

-JEAN J. ROUSSEAU

CREATION	WORTH	LOVE & ACCEPTANCE	GRATITUDE	GENEROSITY	ABUNDANCE

Do you have an expectation of yourself that sucks the joy out of your life?

How can we send the highest love to others if we do not have it for ourselves?

-PRENTICE MULFORD

CREATION	WORTH	LOVE & ACCEPTANCE	GRATITUDE	GENEROSITY	ABUNDANCE

What do you have an abundance of that you are not committed to, or do not enjoy?

Perception is a learned phenomenon.
—DEEPAK CHOPRA

APRIL 5

CREATION	WORTH	LOVE & ACCEPTANCE	GRATITUDE	GENEROSITY	ABUNDANCE

Who are you scared to love?

If I am not for myself, who will be for me?

-HILLEL

APRIL 6

CREATION	WORTH	LOVE & ACCEPTANCE	GRATITUDE	GENEROSITY	ABUNDANCE

What is a service you receive that you are grateful for?

Doubts arise because of the absense of surrender...
-RAMANA MAHARISHI

APRIL 7

CREATION	WORTH	LOVE & ACCEPTANCE	GRATITUDE	GENEROSITY	ABUNDANCE

What do you love about your father?

Only love can be divided endlessly
and still not be diminished.

-ANNE MORROW LINDBERGH

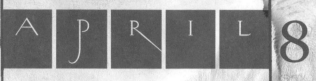

APRIL 8

CREATION	WORTH	LOVE & ACCEPTANCE	GRATITUDE	GENEROSITY	ABUNDANCE

Consider that our holding onto
things limits receiving all
that is in store for us.

I'mperfect.
-JON MARRO

APRIL 9

CREATION	WORTH	LOVE & ACCEPTANCE	GRATITUDE	GENEROSITY	ABUNDANCE

Do you have opinions or do opinions have you?

If you could love enough you would be the happiest and most powerful being in the world.

-EMMET FOX

APRIL 10

CREATION	WORTH	LOVE & ACCEPTANCE	GRATITUDE	GENEROSITY	ABUNDANCE

What experience is created by words like: cheap, expensive, want, get, or have?

Gratitude is the fruit of great cultivation.

-SAMUEL JOHNSON

CREATION	WORTH	LOVE & ACCEPTANCE	GRATITUDE	GENEROSITY	ABUNDANCE

Who do you honor as a contribution to your life?

Don't take anything personally.

-DON MIGUEL RUIZ

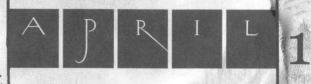

APRIL 12

CREATION	WORTH	LOVE & ACCEPTANCE	GRATITUDE	GENEROSITY	ABUNDANCE

Who do you take for granted?

I murmured because I had no shoes, until I met a man that had no feet.

-PERSIAN PROVERB

CREATION	WORTH	LOVE & ACCEPTANCE	GRATITUDE	GENEROSITY	ABUNDANCE

Say out loud three times:
I am the worthiness of:
(Spirit Word)

Start a huge foolish project like Noah. It makes absolutely no difference what people think of you.

—RUMI

CREATION	WORTH	LOVE & ACCEPTANCE	GRATITUDE	GENEROSITY	ABUNDANCE

Today contribute some form of supply (i.e. money, time, etc.) to EVERY request you receive.

Nothing is enough to a man for whom enough is too little.

-EPICURUS

APRIL 15

CREATION	WORTH	LOVE & ACCEPTANCE	GRATITUDE	GENEROSITY	ABUNDANCE

Are you winning the game of living an inspired life?

Unless I love something it will not reveal itself to me.

— RUDOLPH STEINER

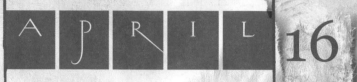

APRIL 16

CREATION	WORTH	LOVE & ACCEPTANCE	GRATITUDE	GENEROSITY	ABUNDANCE

What financial situation of yours are you not being fully responsible for?

It is impossible to be negative
while we are giving thanks.

-DONALD CURTIS

CREATION	WORTH	LOVE & ACCEPTANCE	GRATITUDE	GENEROSITY	ABUNDANCE

Make up something that empowers you.

Safe is a sedative.

-MATTHEW ENGELHART

CREATION	WORTH	LOVE & ACCEPTANCE	GRATITUDE	GENEROSITY	ABUNDANCE

Is there anything you are TOO grateful for?

Gratitude is the sign of noble souls.

-AESOP

APRIL 19

CREATION	WORTH	LOVE & ACCEPTANCE	GRATITUDE	GENEROSITY	ABUNDANCE

Do you adore the person in the mirror?

Nothing real can be threatened, nothing unreal exists.
-A COURSE IN MIRACLES

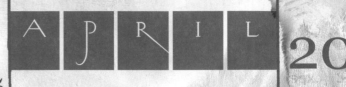

APRIL 20

CREATION	WORTH	LOVE & ACCEPTANCE	GRATITUDE	GENEROSITY	ABUNDANCE

What do you imagine your life would be like if you experienced being completely provided for?

Man's chief work is to praise God.

-AUGUSTINE

CREATION	WORTH	LOVE & ACCEPTANCE	GRATITUDE	GENEROSITY	ABUNDANCE

Can you bow to all the ways you are and all the ways you're not?

Be sure your prayer is not a
desire to improve God's universe.
-JOEL GOLDSMITH

CREATION	WORTH	LOVE & ACCEPTANCE	GRATITUDE	GENEROSITY	ABUNDANCE

In what ways can you
be grateful for a parking
ticket?

Gratitude is the memory of the heart.

-JEAN B. MASSIEU

APRIL 23

CREATION	WORTH	LOVE & ACCEPTANCE	GRATITUDE	GENEROSITY	ABUNDANCE

For whom does your existence make a difference?

There is no need to run outside for better seeing, nor to peer from a window. Rather abide at the center of your being; for the more you leave it, the less you learn.

-LAO TZU

APRIL 24

CREATION	WORTH	LOVE & ACCEPTANCE	GRATITUDE	GENEROSITY	ABUNDANCE

Where in your life are you trying to force an outcome, get somewhere, manipulate, or manage the circumstances?

Pray without ceasing,
in everything give thanks.
–THESSALONIANS 5:17

APRIL

25

CREATION	WORTH	LOVE & ACCEPTANCE	GRATITUDE	GENEROSITY	ABUNDANCE

What would be possible if you weren't concerned with what others thought?

There is enough in the world for
everyone's need;
but not for everyone's greed... —GHANDI

APRIL 26

CREATION	WORTH	LOVE & ACCEPTANCE	GRATITUDE	GENEROSITY	ABUNDANCE

Say out loud three times:
I acknowledge the Divine in
everyone and everything.

A thankful presence is a divine present.

-MATTHEW ENGELHART

APRIL 27

CREATION	WORTH	LOVE & ACCEPTANCE	GRATITUDE	GENEROSITY	ABUNDANCE

What if you celebrated everything as a part of your awakening?

Trying to help the world without knowing yourself will be just like a blind man trying to treat diseases of the eyes of others. First, clear your own eyes.

-RAMANA MAHARSHI

CREATION	WORTH	LOVE & ACCEPTANCE	GRATITUDE	GENEROSITY	ABUNDANCE

Whom can you express your appreciation to for the contribution they have made to your life?

A thankful heart is not only the greatest
virtue but the parent of all other virtues.

-CICERO

APRIL 29

CREATION	WORTH	LOVE & ACCEPTANCE	GRATITUDE	GENEROSITY	ABUNDANCE

What is beyond right
and wrong?

Only the threatened attack.

-A COURSE IN MIRACLES

CREATION	WORTH	LOVE & ACCEPTANCE	GRATITUDE	GENEROSITY	ABUNDANCE

Write down any resistance you have to being rich.

THE PERSON WHO HAS STOPPED BEING THANKFUL HAS FALLEN ASLEEP IN LIFE. —Robert Louis Stevenson

MAY 1

CREATION	WORTH	LOVE & ACCEPTANCE	GRATITUDE	GENEROSITY	ABUNDANCE

What about life
don't you trust?

NOW FAITH IS THE SUBSTANCE OF THINGS HOPED FOR, THE EVIDENCE OF THINGS NOT SEEN.

=Hebrews 11:1

MAY 2

CREATION	WORTH	LOVE & ACCEPTANCE	GRATITUDE	GENEROSITY	ABUNDANCE

What can you thank yourself for?

IF THE ONLY PRAYER YOU SAY IN YOUR WHOLE LIFE IS THANK YOU, THAT WOULD SUFFICE —Meister Eckhart

MAY 3

CREATION	WORTH	LOVE & ACCEPTANCE	GRATITUDE	GENEROSITY	ABUNDANCE

What would like to be acknowledged for?

TO KEEP A LAMP BURNING WE HAVE TO KEEP PUTTING OIL IN IT.

— Mother Teresa

MAY 4

CREATION	WORTH	LOVE & ACCEPTANCE	GRATITUDE	GENEROSITY	ABUNDANCE

When you share something, where does it go anyway?

THE BEGINNING OF MAN'S REBELLION AGAINST GOD WAS, AND IS, THE LACK OF A THANKFUL HEART. —Francis Schaeffer

MAY 5

CREATION	WORTH	LOVE & ACCEPTANCE	GRATITUDE	GENEROSITY	ABUNDANCE

Do you have enough right now?

WAKE AT DAWN WITH A WINGED HEART AND GIVE THANKS FOR ANOTHER DAY OF LOVING. -Kahlil Gibran

MAY 6

CREATION	WORTH	LOVE & ACCEPTANCE	GRATITUDE	GENEROSITY	ABUNDANCE

How could you look upon being rich as an opportunity?

THANKSGIVING IS A SURE INDEX OF SPIRITUAL HEALTH.

— Maurice Dametz

MAY 7

CREATION	WORTH	LOVE & ACCEPTANCE	GRATITUDE	GENEROSITY	ABUNDANCE

If you were certain that life was eternal and unfolding perfectly what would you take on?

WHATEVER YOU LOVE YOU ARE.

-Rumi

MAY 8

CREATION	WORTH	LOVE & ACCEPTANCE	GRATITUDE	GENEROSITY	ABUNDANCE

Can you see that everyone has worth and value?

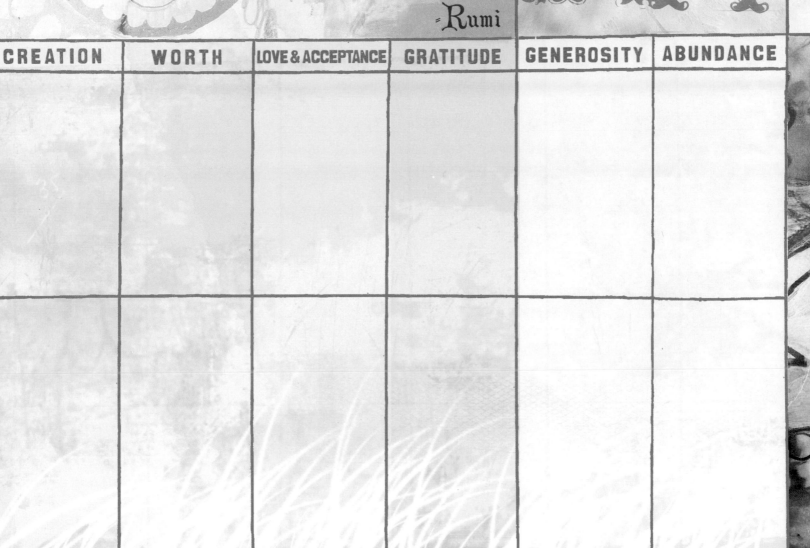

THE SEEDS OF DISCOURAGEMENT WILL NOT GROW IN A THANKFUL HEART.

— Anonymous

MAY 9

CREATION	WORTH	LOVE & ACCEPTANCE	GRATITUDE	GENEROSITY	ABUNDANCE

Next time you are tired, ask yourself: "What am I resisting?"

AH, BUT A MAN'S REACH SHOULD EXCEED HIS GRASP, OR WHAT'S A HEAVEN FOR?
— Robert Browning

MAY 10

CREATION	WORTH	LOVE & ACCEPTANCE	GRATITUDE	GENEROSITY	ABUNDANCE

Can you see all the stuff you have takes up physical, mental, emotional, and/or spiritual space?

ENOUGH IS AS GOOD AS A FEAST.

-John Heywood

MAY 11

CREATION	WORTH	LOVE & ACCEPTANCE	GRATITUDE	GENEROSITY	ABUNDANCE

What do you love about being extraordinary?

JOY IS THE EMOTION EXCITED BY THE EXPECTANCY OF GOOD.

— Ernest Holmes

MAY 12

CREATION	WORTH	LOVE & ACCEPTANCE	GRATITUDE	GENEROSITY	ABUNDANCE

Can you see that money itself is neutral, and that your experience of money is what you bring to it?

WHILE YOU FEAR MISSING A MEAL, YOU AREN'T FULLY AWARE OF THE MEALS YOU DO EAT.
— Dan Millman

MAY 13

CREATION	WORTH	LOVE & ACCEPTANCE	GRATITUDE	GENEROSITY	ABUNDANCE

Say out loud three times:
My life is a picture of my thoughts, speech, beliefs, actions, and attitudes. I am grateful now.

ALL THERE IS IS LOVE, EVERYTHING ELSE IS OUR RESISTANCE TO IT.

— Terces Engelhart

MAY 14

CREATION	WORTH	LOVE & ACCEPTANCE	GRATITUDE	GENEROSITY	ABUNDANCE

Today express gratitude to someone you don't know.

IF YOU COUNT ALL YOUR ASSETS YOU ALWAYS SHOW A PROFIT.

— Robert Quillen

MAY 15

CREATION	WORTH	LOVE & ACCEPTANCE	GRATITUDE	GENEROSITY	ABUNDANCE

With what daily ritual do you celebrate yourself?

EVERYTHING THAT HAPPENS TO US HAPPENS BY CHOICE.

— James Twyman

MAY 16

CREATION	WORTH	LOVE & ACCEPTANCE	GRATITUDE	GENEROSITY	ABUNDANCE

What is something you could do that would contribute to your community?

MOST HUMAN BEINGS HAVE AN ALMOST INFINITE CAPACITY FOR TAKING THINGS FOR GRANTED.

-Aldous Huxley

MAY 17

CREATION	WORTH	LOVE & ACCEPTANCE	GRATITUDE	GENEROSITY	ABUNDANCE

What do you care about?

A MIRACLE IS THE SPONTANEOUS EXPRESSION OF YOUR DIVINE NATURE.

—James Twyman

MAY 18

CREATION	WORTH	LOVE & ACCEPTANCE	GRATITUDE	GENEROSITY	ABUNDANCE

Today look everyone in the eyes you exchange money with and say "Thank you for being here."

GRATITUDE IS THE BOTTOM LINE OF HAPPINESS.

—Lewis B. Smedes

MAY 19

CREATION	WORTH	LOVE & ACCEPTANCE	GRATITUDE	GENEROSITY	ABUNDANCE

Are you willing to stand for another's life without their consent?

IT IS SIMPLE TO FACE YOUR FEARS
WHEN YOU STAY IN THE MOMENT;
FEARS DON'T LIVE IN THE
PRESENT MOMENT. —Terces Engelhart

MAY 20

CREATION	WORTH	LOVE & ACCEPTANCE	GRATITUDE	GENEROSITY	ABUNDANCE

What do you imagine your life would be like if you could simply trust in every experience?

WHO DOES NOT THANK FOR LITTLE WILL NOT THANK FOR MUCH.

~Estonian Proverb

MAY 21

CREATION	WORTH	LOVE & ACCEPTANCE	GRATITUDE	GENEROSITY	ABUNDANCE

Can you embrace all of yourself?

THERE IS ONLY ONE PROBLEM AND ONE SOLUTION. THE PROBLEM IS THAT WE BELIEVE WE'RE ALONE. THE SOLUTION IS THAT WE'RE NOT. —James Twyman

MAY 22

CREATION	WORTH	LOVE & ACCEPTANCE	GRATITUDE	GENEROSITY	ABUNDANCE

What is a circumstance you are currently challenged by that you can be grateful for?

GRATITUDE IS A MAGIC WAND.

-Jan Kinney

MAY 23

CREATION	WORTH	LOVE & ACCEPTANCE	GRATITUDE	GENEROSITY	ABUNDANCE

Does it make any sense to judge your creator's creation?

BEING GRATEFUL ISN'T ABOUT BEING GRATEFUL FOR SOMETHING, IT'S ABOUT BEING GRATEFUL FOR EVERYTHING.

-Terces Engelhart

CREATION	WORTH	LOVE & ACCEPTANCE	GRATITUDE	GENEROSITY	ABUNDANCE

What can you thank or be grateful to your mother for?

BEING GRATEFUL I SEE ALL I HAVE TO GIVE AWAY.

—Matthew Engelhart

MAY 25

CREATION	WORTH	LOVE & ACCEPTANCE	GRATITUDE	GENEROSITY	ABUNDANCE

Who you "be" is your canvas. What are you going to paint?

BE SURE YOUR REQUESTS OCCUR AS OPPORTUNITIES FOR OTHERS.

—Sacred Commerce

MAY 26

CREATION	WORTH	LOVE & ACCEPTANCE	GRATITUDE	GENEROSITY	ABUNDANCE

Say out loud three times:

_____Spirit Word_____ is present everywhere

as everything I see and don't see.

WHEN IN DOUBT, BE GRATEFUL.

— Matthew Engelhart

MAY 27

CREATION	WORTH	LOVE & ACCEPTANCE	GRATITUDE	GENEROSITY	ABUNDANCE

How do you move from your head to your heart?

KEEP KNOCKING, AND THE JOY INSIDE WILL
EVENTUALLY OPEN A WINDOW AND LOOK
OUT TO SEE WHO'S THERE.
—Rumi

MAY 28

CREATION	WORTH	LOVE & ACCEPTANCE	GRATITUDE	GENEROSITY	ABUNDANCE

What is a belief you have about yourself that you like?

THERE IS NO FEAR IN LOVE;
BUT PERFECT LOVE CASTETH
OUT FEAR... ~John IV:LVIII

MAY 29

CREATION	WORTH	LOVE & ACCEPTANCE	GRATITUDE	GENEROSITY	ABUNDANCE

What do you give
your life to?

DEATH IS THE CENTRAL DREAM FROM WHICH ALL ILLUSIONS STEM. *A Course In Miracles*

CREATION	WORTH	LOVE & ACCEPTANCE	GRATITUDE	GENEROSITY	ABUNDANCE

What can you thank a family member for?

LOVE IS THE ENERGIZING ELIXIR OF THE UNIVERSE, THE CAUSE AND EFFECT OF ALL HARMONIES.

— Rumi

MAY 31

CREATION	WORTH	LOVE & ACCEPTANCE	GRATITUDE	GENEROSITY	ABUNDANCE

What fact about nature inspires awe?

IF YOU
ARE IN
THE NOW,
YOU'LL KNOW HOW.

–BARON BAPTISTE

Opulence is the law of the universe, an abundant supply for every need if nothing is put in the way of its coming.

-Ralph W. Trine

JUNE 1

CREATION	WORTH	LOVE & ACCEPTANCE	GRATITUDE	GENEROSITY	ABUNDANCE

Can you consider that a leader apologizes first and takes 100% responsibility?

Turn your face to the sun and the shadows will fall behind you.

-Maori Proverb

JUNE 2

CREATION	WORTH	LOVE & ACCEPTANCE	GRATITUDE	GENEROSITY	ABUNDANCE

Today express your gratitude in a letter, email, or phone call to an institution you admire.

Those who are free of resentful thoughts surely find peace.

-Buddha

JUNE 3

CREATION	WORTH	LOVE & ACCEPTANCE	GRATITUDE	GENEROSITY	ABUNDANCE

Where in your life can you take the lead?

'We have thought that outside things controlled us, when all the time we have had that within which could have changed everything and given us freedom from bondage.
-Ernest Holmes

JUNE 4

CREATION	WORTH	LOVE & ACCEPTANCE	GRATITUDE	GENEROSITY	ABUNDANCE

Can you see what you keep inside keeps you from experiencing the flow of abundance?

The only genuine love worthy of the name is unconditional...
-John Powell

JUNE 5

CREATION	WORTH	LOVE & ACCEPTANCE	GRATITUDE	GENEROSITY	ABUNDANCE

If heaven is a choice now, what do you choose?

We are chemists in the laboratory of the Infinite. What, then, shall we create?

-Ernest Holmes

JUNE 6

CREATION	WORTH	LOVE & ACCEPTANCE	GRATITUDE	GENEROSITY	ABUNDANCE

Say out loud to yourself three times in the mirror: "I love and accept myself for everything I am and everything I'm not."

Love is an act of endless forgiveness.

-Peter. Ustinov

JUNE 7

CREATION	WORTH	LOVE & ACCEPTANCE	GRATITUDE	GENEROSITY	ABUNDANCE

Give a stranger a hug today.

To fall into habit is to begin to cease to be.

-Miguel de Unamuno

JUNE 8

CREATION	WORTH	LOVE & ACCEPTANCE	GRATITUDE	GENEROSITY	ABUNDANCE

Today practice being your own best friend.

Love is the strongest force the world possesses, and yet it is the humblest imaginable.

-Mohandas Gandhi

JUNE 9

CREATION	WORTH	LOVE & ACCEPTANCE	GRATITUDE	GENEROSITY	ABUNDANCE

What aspect of your humanity have you failed to embrace?

When you change the way you see things, the things you see change.

-Anonymous

JUNE 10

CREATION	WORTH	LOVE & ACCEPTANCE	GRATITUDE	GENEROSITY	ABUNDANCE

Who would "Spirit" deny?
Who are you to deny
"Spirit" as anyone?

Judge not less ye be judged.

-Matthew 7:1

JUNE 11

CREATION	WORTH	LOVE & ACCEPTANCE	GRATITUDE	GENEROSITY	ABUNDANCE

Does avoidance of conflict cost you your power?

The natural healing force in each one of us is the greatest force in getting well.

-Hippocrates

JUNE 12

CREATION	WORTH	LOVE & ACCEPTANCE	GRATITUDE	GENEROSITY	ABUNDANCE

Find a way to carpool today.

We are shaped and fashioned by what we love...
                                    -Johann W. Goethe

JUNE 13

CREATION	WORTH	LOVE & ACCEPTANCE	GRATITUDE	GENEROSITY	ABUNDANCE

Say out loud three times:
I release any thoughts,
speech, beliefs, actions, or
attitudes of being unworthy.

You could not step twice into the same river;
for other waters are ever flowing on to you.

-Heraclitus

JUNE 14

CREATION	WORTH	LOVE & ACCEPTANCE	GRATITUDE	GENEROSITY	ABUNDANCE

Do you believe people can be trusted? If not, then who do you trust?

Take away love and our earth is a tomb.

-Robert Browning

JUNE 15

CREATION	WORTH	LOVE & ACCEPTANCE	GRATITUDE	GENEROSITY	ABUNDANCE

What would life look like if you loved your least favorite parts of you?

There is no chance, no destiny, no fate, that can circumvent or hinder or control the firm resolve of a determined soul.
-Ella Wheeler Wilcox

JUNE 16

CREATION	WORTH	LOVE & ACCEPTANCE	GRATITUDE	GENEROSITY	ABUNDANCE

Express your gratitude for a historical figure or event that has contributed to your life.

Happiness is a function of accepting what is.

-Werner. Erhard

JUNE 17

CREATION	WORTH	LOVE & ACCEPTANCE	GRATITUDE	GENEROSITY	ABUNDANCE

What is something you love to do that you either deny yourself or just don't seem to get around to?

Love is a fire and I am wood.

-Rumi

JUNE 18

CREATION	WORTH	LOVE & ACCEPTANCE	GRATITUDE	GENEROSITY	ABUNDANCE

Can you see that
Love is bigger than
YOUR personal views?

Love is the doorway through which the human soul passes from selfishness to service and from solitude to kinship with all mankind.

-Unknown

JUNE 19

CREATION	WORTH	LOVE & ACCEPTANCE	GRATITUDE	GENEROSITY	ABUNDANCE

Express gratitude for some aspect of nature that completely supports your existence (ie. photosynthesis, sunshine, rain...).

Love is the self-givingness of the Spirit through the desire of life to express itself in terms of creation.
-Ernest Holmes

JUNE 20

CREATION	WORTH	LOVE & ACCEPTANCE	GRATITUDE	GENEROSITY	ABUNDANCE

Do you celebrate everyone's success or do you find yourself (maybe even secretly) being jealous or competitive?

*When God sends rain,
rain is my choice.*

-James W. Riley

JUNE 21

CREATION	WORTH	LOVE & ACCEPTANCE	GRATITUDE	GENEROSITY	ABUNDANCE

What is something you say you don't "need" that you would really like or enjoy having or receiving?

When I dipped into the future far as human eye could see; saw the vision of the world and all the wonder that would be. -Lord Alfred Tennyson

JUNE 22

CREATION	WORTH	LOVE & ACCEPTANCE	GRATITUDE	GENEROSITY	ABUNDANCE

If forgiveness means "to give as before", whom have you stopped giving to?

To oppose something is to maintain it.

-Ursula K. Le Guin

JUNE 23

CREATION	WORTH	LOVE & ACCEPTANCE	GRATITUDE	GENEROSITY	ABUNDANCE

How do you create yourself as less than worthy?

Divinity is in its omniscience and omnipotence like a wheel, a circle, a whole, that can neither be understood, nor divided, nor begun nor ended.

-Hildegard of Bingen

JUNE 24

CREATION	WORTH	LOVE & ACCEPTANCE	GRATITUDE	GENEROSITY	ABUNDANCE

What could you consciously practice loving about yourself?

JUNE 25

Minds were designed for carrying out the orders of the heart.

-Emmanuel

CREATION	WORTH	LOVE & ACCEPTANCE	GRATITUDE	GENEROSITY	ABUNDANCE

Remember you are not the chatter in your head. you are the one who is listening to it.

Joy has come to live with me. How can I be sad? I do so love Thy presence, which is joy within me.
-Ernest Holmes

JUNE 26

CREATION	WORTH	LOVE & ACCEPTANCE	GRATITUDE	GENEROSITY	ABUNDANCE

Say out loud three times: I adore myself and others as the whole of life now.

The great Way is not difficult if you do not cling to good and bad. Just let go of your opinions and everything will be clear.

-Third Zen Patriarch

JUNE 27

CREATION	WORTH	LOVE & ACCEPTANCE	GRATITUDE	GENEROSITY	ABUNDANCE

Who is one person you honor? What is stopping you from honoring every person in that same way?

Happiness is a butterfly, which, when pursued, is always just beyond your grasp, but which if you will sit down quietly, may alight upon you.
-Nathaniel Hawthorne

CREATION	WORTH	LOVE & ACCEPTANCE	GRATITUDE	GENEROSITY	ABUNDANCE

Consider that you are the one creating all of your "shoulds" or "have tos".

I have learned silence from the talkative, tolerance from the intolerant, and kindness from the unkind. I should not be ungrateful to those teachers.

-Kahlil Gibran

JUNE 29

CREATION	WORTH	LOVE & ACCEPTANCE	GRATITUDE	GENEROSITY	ABUNDANCE

What is a quality you often acknowledge or compliment others for? Practice acknowledging yourself for that same quality.

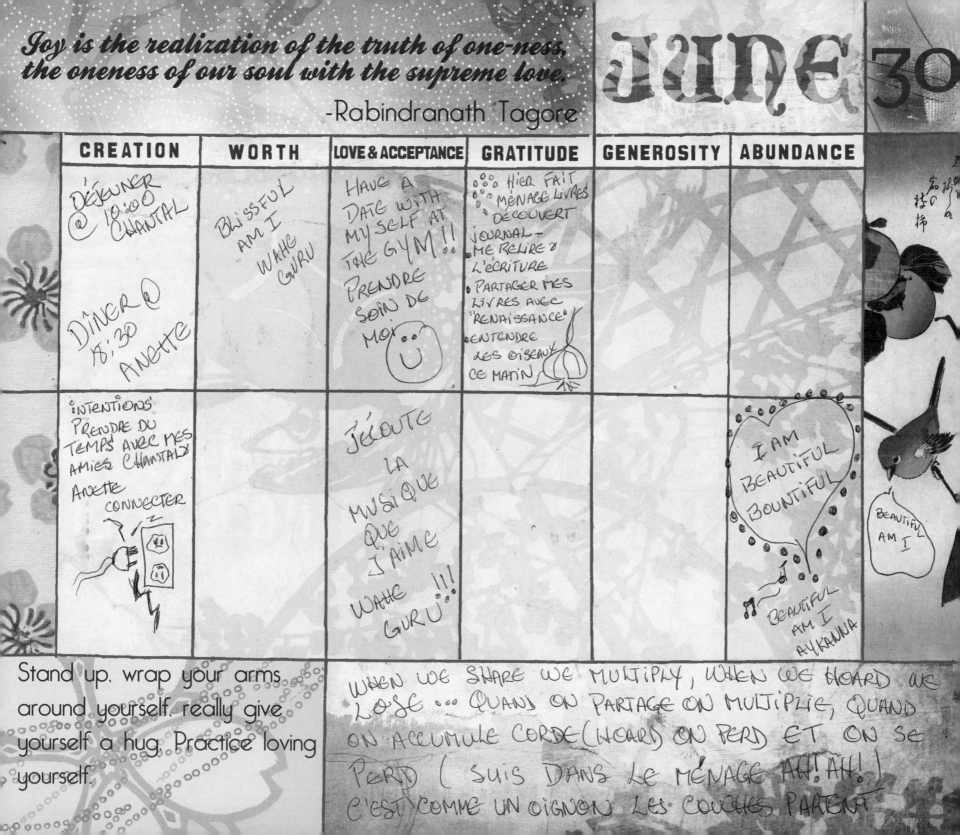

Joy is the realization of the truth of one-ness, the oneness of our soul with the supreme love.

-Rabindranath Tagore

JUNE 30

CREATION	WORTH	LOVE & ACCEPTANCE	GRATITUDE	GENEROSITY	ABUNDANCE
DÉJEUNER @ 10:00 CHANTAL DÎNER @ 18:30 ANETTE	BLISSFUL AM I WAHE GURU	HAVE A DATE WITH MYSELF AT THE GYM !!! PRENDRE SOIN DE MOI	°°° HIER FAIT °°° MÉNAGE LIVRES ° DÉCOUVERT JOURNAL – ME RELIRE & L'ÉCRITURE ° PARTAGER MES LIVRES AVEC "RENAISSANCE" ° ENTENDRE LES OISEAUX CE MATIN		
'INTENTIONS' PRENDRE DU TEMPS AVEC MES AMIES (CHANTAL) ANETTE CONNECTER		J'ÉCOUTE LA MUSIQUE QUE J'AIME WAHE GURU !!!!			I AM BEAUTIFUL BOUNTIFUL BEAUTIFUL AM I BEAUTIFUL AM I AYKANNA

Stand up, wrap your arms around yourself, really give yourself a hug. Practice loving yourself.

WHEN WE SHARE WE MULTIPLY, WHEN WE HOARD WE LOSE ... QUAND ON PARTAGE ON MULTIPLIE, QUAND ON ACCUMULE CORDE (HOARD) ON PERD ET ON SE PERD (SUIS DANS LE MÉNAGE AH! AH!) C'EST COMME UN OIGNON LES COUCHES PARENT

PEOPLE SAY THAT WHAT WE
ARE SEEKING IS A MEANING FOR LIFE

I DON'T THINK THIS IS WHAT
WE'RE REALLY SEEKING. I THINK WHAT WE'RE
REALLY SEEKING IS AN EXPERIENCE OF BEING ALIVE

—JOSEPH CAMPBELL

CONSIDER THE AWAKENING IS ALREADY HAPPENING, EITHER CONSCIOUSLY OR UNCONSCIOUSLY.
—Sacred Commerce

CREATION	WORTH	LOVE & ACCEPTANCE	GRATITUDE	GENEROSITY	ABUNDANCE

Where are you avoiding playing a bigger game?

THERE IS POWER AND FREEDOM IN BEING THE FOOL.

-George Eliot

JULY 2

CREATION	WORTH	LOVE & ACCEPTANCE	GRATITUDE	GENEROSITY	ABUNDANCE

Where are you confused?

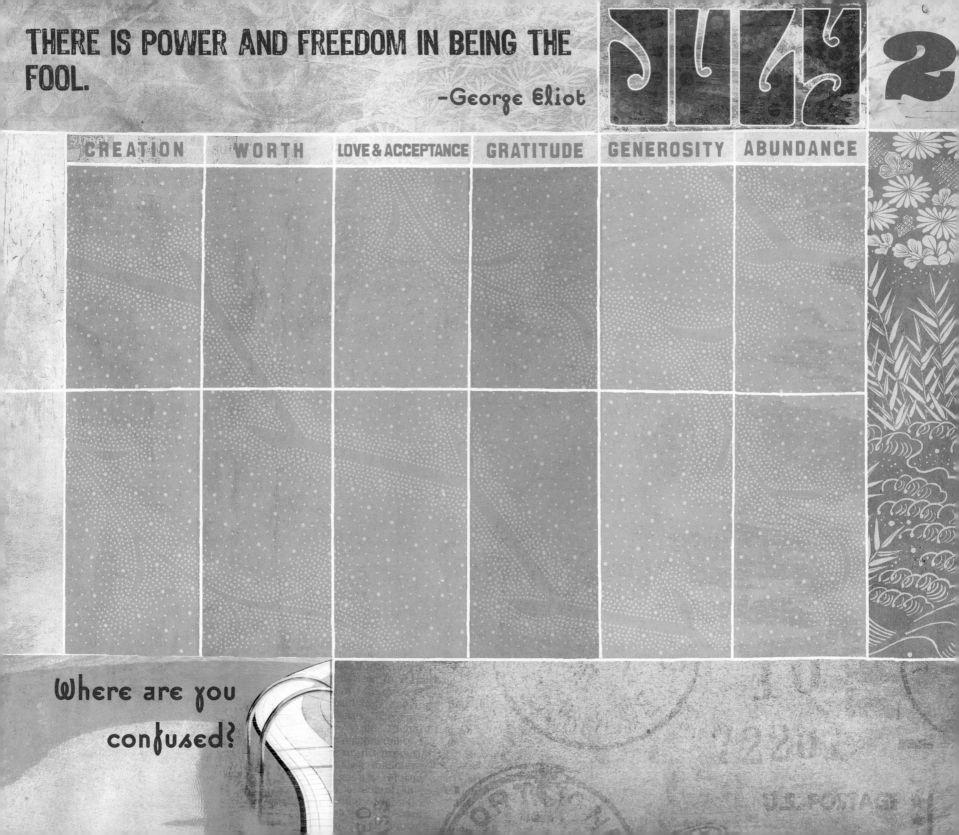

JULY 3

I USED TO SAY LIFE WAS SHORT, I DON'T KNOW WHAT THAT WAS FOR. THINGS GONNA WAIT FOR ME.

-The Makepeace Brothers

CREATION	WORTH	LOVE & ACCEPTANCE	GRATITUDE	GENEROSITY	ABUNDANCE

Who are you seeing in a new light?

GREAT PEOPLE ARE THOSE WHO MAKE OTHERS FEEL THAT THEY TOO, CAN BECOME GREAT.

-Mark Twain

JULY 4

CREATION	WORTH	LOVE & ACCEPTANCE	GRATITUDE	GENEROSITY	ABUNDANCE

Where do you see romance?

A MAN IS WHAT HE THINKS ABOUT ALL DAY LONG.

-Ralph Waldo Emerson

JULY 5

CREATION	WORTH	LOVE & ACCEPTANCE	GRATITUDE	GENEROSITY	ABUNDANCE

What part of yourself are you denying?

MOST PEOPLE ARE ABOUT AS HAPPY AS THEY MAKE UP THEIR MINDS TO BE.

-Abraham Lincoln

JULY

6

CREATION	WORTH	LOVE & ACCEPTANCE	GRATITUDE	GENEROSITY	ABUNDANCE

What is your best trait?

HAPPINESS LIES IN THE FULFILLMENT OF THE SPIRIT THROUGH THE BODY.

-Cyril Connolly

JULY 7

CREATION	WORTH	LOVE & ACCEPTANCE	GRATITUDE	GENEROSITY	ABUNDANCE

Who are you proud of?

THE LOVE OF ONESELF IS THE BEGINNING OF A LIFELONG ROMANCE.

-Oscar Wilde

JULY 8

CREATION	WORTH	LOVE & ACCEPTANCE	GRATITUDE	GENEROSITY	ABUNDANCE

What is magical about your life?

TO DREAM OF THE PERSON YOU WOULD LIKE TO BE IS TO WASTE THE PERSON YOU ARE.
—Anonymous

JULY 9

CREATION	WORTH	LOVE & ACCEPTANCE	GRATITUDE	GENEROSITY	ABUNDANCE

Where are you not caring for yourself?

WONDER IS THE BASIS OF WORSHIP.

-Thomas Carlyle

JULY 10

CREATION	WORTH	LOVE & ACCEPTANCE	GRATITUDE	GENEROSITY	ABUNDANCE

What are you pretending?

JULY 11

I DISCOVERED THE SECRET OF THE SEA IN MEDITATION UPON A DEWDROP.

-Kahlil Gibran

CREATION	WORTH	LOVE & ACCEPTANCE	GRATITUDE	GENEROSITY	ABUNDANCE

Who idolizes you?

WE ARE ALL WANDERERS ON THIS EARTH. OUR HEARTS ARE FULL OF WONDER, AND OUR SOULS ARE DEEP WITH DREAMS.

-Gypsy Saying

JULY 12

CREATION	WORTH	LOVE & ACCEPTANCE	GRATITUDE	GENEROSITY	ABUNDANCE

What discovery are you celebrating?

U.S. POSTAGE

IF YOU WANT TO BE HAPPY, BE.

-Leo Tolstoy

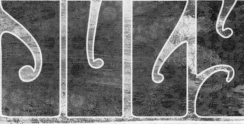

JULY 13

CREATION	WORTH	LOVE & ACCEPTANCE	GRATITUDE	GENEROSITY	ABUNDANCE

Where are you choosing to make a difference?

REAL GENEROSITY TOWARD THE FUTURE LIES IN GIVING ALL TO THE PRESENT. —Albert Camus

JULY 14

CREATION	WORTH	LOVE & ACCEPTANCE	GRATITUDE	GENEROSITY	ABUNDANCE

What do you teach?

U.S. POSTAGE

WORRY NEVER ROBS TOMORROW OF ITS
SORROW, IT ONLY SAPS TODAY OF ITS
STRENGTH.
                                    —AJ Cronin

JULY 15

CREATION	WORTH	LOVE & ACCEPTANCE	GRATITUDE	GENEROSITY	ABUNDANCE

How can today
teach
tomorrow?

IT IS GOOD TO HAVE AN END TO JOURNEY TOWARDS, BUT IT IS THE JOURNEY THAT MATTERS IN THE END.

-Ursula K. Le Guin

JULY 16

CREATION	WORTH	LOVE & ACCEPTANCE	GRATITUDE	GENEROSITY	ABUNDANCE

How do you stop yourself from getting what you want?

NOBODY HAS MEASURED, NOT EVEN POETS, HOW MUCH THE HEART CAN HOLD.

-Zelda Fitzgerald

17

CREATION	WORTH	LOVE & ACCEPTANCE	GRATITUDE	GENEROSITY	ABUNDANCE

What do you love about community?

AN UNHURRIED SENSE OF TIME IS IN ITSELF A FORM OF WEALTH.

-Bonnie Friedman

JULY 18

CREATION	WORTH	LOVE & ACCEPTANCE	GRATITUDE	GENEROSITY	ABUNDANCE

Who could you choose to see differently?

IF THREE OF US TRAVEL TOGETHER, I SHALL FIND TWO TEACHERS.

—Confucius

JULY 19

CREATION	WORTH	LOVE & ACCEPTANCE	GRATITUDE	GENEROSITY	ABUNDANCE

Where have you fallen asleep to your dreams?

HE WHO WOULD HAVE BEAUTIFUL ROSES IN HIS GARDEN MUST HAVE BEAUTIFUL ROSES IN HIS HEART.

—S.R. Hole

JULY 20

CREATION	WORTH	LOVE & ACCEPTANCE	GRATITUDE	GENEROSITY	ABUNDANCE

Where are you resisting growth?

MIRRORS SHOULD REFLECT A LITTLE BEFORE THROWING BACK IMAGES.

-Jean Cocteau

JULY 21

CREATION	WORTH	LOVE & ACCEPTANCE	GRATITUDE	GENEROSITY	ABUNDANCE

When do you feel powerful?

HE MAKES THINGS EASIER FOR HIMSELF WHO MAKES THINGS EASIER FOR OTHERS.

-Anonymous

JULY

22

CREATION	WORTH	LOVE & ACCEPTANCE	GRATITUDE	GENEROSITY	ABUNDANCE

What is keeping you from being fulfilled?

WE THINK IT IS VERY PRIMITIVE FOR A CHILD
TO HAVE ONLY TWO PARENTS.
         -Australian Aboriginal Elder

JULY 23

CREATION	WORTH	LOVE & ACCEPTANCE	GRATITUDE	GENEROSITY	ABUNDANCE

What is your
prayer for
the world?

FIND THE SEED AT THE BOTTOM OF YOUR HEART AND BRING FORTH A FLOWER.
-Shigenori Kameoka

JULY 24

CREATION	WORTH	LOVE & ACCEPTANCE	GRATITUDE	GENEROSITY	ABUNDANCE

Where are you resisting more?

TODAY IS THE 365TH DAY OF THE THIRTEEN MOON CALENDAR, A MAYAN SYSTEM THAT MEASURES THE YEAR IN THIRTEEN MONTHS OF 28 DAYS EACH: A PERPETUAL CALENDAR OF 52 PERFECT WEEKS, WITH A TOTAL OF 364 DAYS. THE 365TH DAY, THE "DAY OUT OF TIME", IS NOT A DAY OF THE WEEK OR MONTH AT ALL, BUT TRULY A *DAY OUT OF TIME*. THIS DAY OF ARTISTIC CELEBRATION IS AN OPPORTUNITY TO CANCEL DEBTS, TO PARDON AND FORGIVE, AND TO CELEBRATE LIFE, PURIFICATION, COMMUNITY, LOVE, AND UNIVERSAL FORGIVENESS OF ALL BEINGS.

JULY 25

CREATION	WORTH	LOVE & ACCEPTANCE	GRATITUDE	GENEROSITY	ABUNDANCE

If you could take on anything today (and you can!) what would you take on getting complete?

JULY 26

I DO NOT ASK FOR THE MEANING OF THE SONG OF A BIRD OR THE RISING OF THE SUN ON A MISTY MORNING. THERE THEY ARE, AND THEY ARE BEAUTIFUL. —Pete Hamill

CREATION	WORTH	LOVE & ACCEPTANCE	GRATITUDE	GENEROSITY	ABUNDANCE

What do you love about where you live?

JULY 27

RELIGION IS SOMETHING INFINITELY SIMPLE, INGENUOUS...
IN THE INFINITE EXTENT OF THE UNIVERSE, IT IS A
DIRECTION OF THE HEART.
                                    —Rainer Maria Rilke

CREATION	WORTH	LOVE & ACCEPTANCE	GRATITUDE	GENEROSITY	ABUNDANCE

If money did not exist what would your life look like?

ALL PRAYERS ARE ANSWERED. WE NEED TO DISTINGUISH BETWEEN A PRAYER UNANSWERED AND ONE NOT ANSWERED HOW OR WHEN WE WOULD LIKE IT TO BE.   -Lloyd Ogilvie

JULY 28

CREATION	WORTH	LOVE & ACCEPTANCE	GRATITUDE	GENEROSITY	ABUNDANCE

Who do you adore?

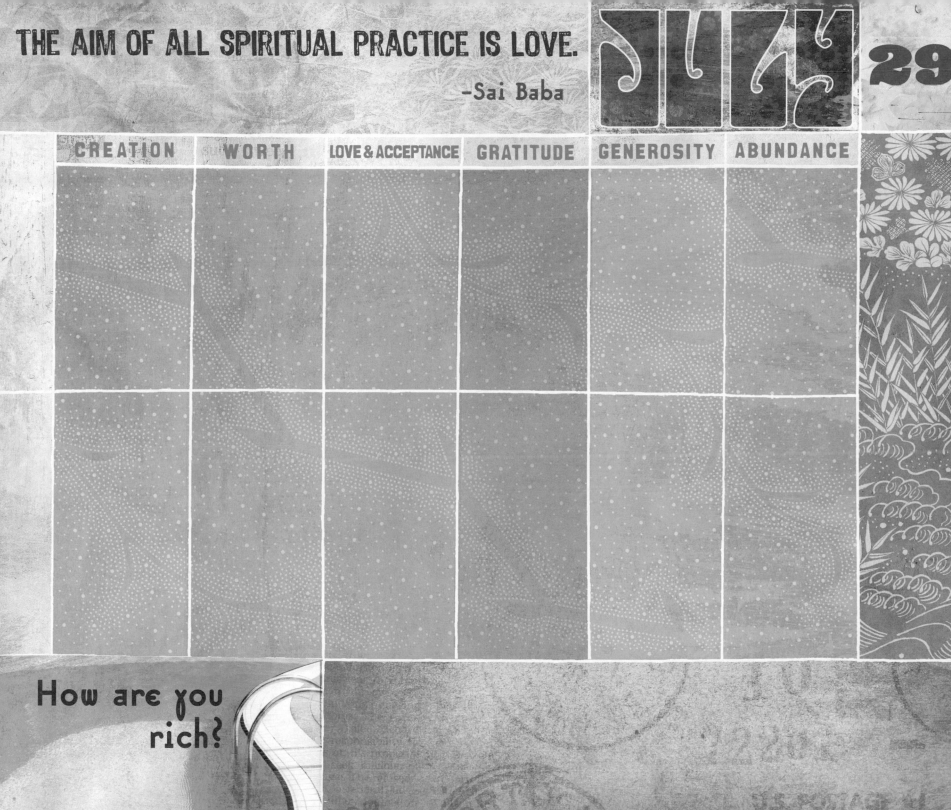

THE AIM OF ALL SPIRITUAL PRACTICE IS LOVE.

–Sai Baba

JULY

29

CREATION	WORTH	LOVE & ACCEPTANCE	GRATITUDE	GENEROSITY	ABUNDANCE

How are you rich?

GOD, I CAN PUSH THE GRASS APART AND LAY
MY FINGER ON THY HEART.
-Edna St. Vincent Millay

JULY 30

CREATION	WORTH	LOVE & ACCEPTANCE	GRATITUDE	GENEROSITY	ABUNDANCE

How do you
rejuvenate
yourself?

NATURE IS THE ART OF GOD.

–Dante

JULY 31

CREATION	WORTH	LOVE & ACCEPTANCE	GRATITUDE	GENEROSITY	ABUNDANCE

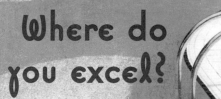

Where do you excel?

AN UNHURRIED SENSE OF TIME IS IN ITSELF A FORM OF WEALTH.

-BONNIE FRIEDMAN

NO LIFE IS SO HARD THAT YOU CAN'T MAKE IT EASIER BY THE WAY YOU TAKE IT. —Ellen Glasgow

AUGUST 1

CREATION	WORTH	LOVE & ACCEPTANCE	GRATITUDE	GENEROSITY	ABUNDANCE

Will you be more generous when you have more money?

IT IS THE SPIRITUAL ALWAYS THAT DETERMINES THE MATERIAL.

—Thomas Carlyle

AUGUST 2

CREATION	WORTH	LOVE & ACCEPTANCE	GRATITUDE	GENEROSITY	ABUNDANCE

Whom do you think creates your experience of life?

CIRCUMSTANCES!
I MAKE CIRCUMSTANCES.

-Napoleon

AUGUST 3

CREATION	WORTH	LOVE & ACCEPTANCE	GRATITUDE	GENEROSITY	ABUNDANCE

*What question is your
life about answering?*

THE HEALING IS ALREADY HAPPENING...WHY NOT EMBRACE IT?

~Terces Engelhart

AUGUST

CREATION	WORTH	LOVE & ACCEPTANCE	GRATITUDE	GENEROSITY	ABUNDANCE

Where are you going?

NO ONE CAN SUFFER LOSS UNLESS IT IS HIS OWN DECISION.

—The Course in Miracles

AUGUST 5

CREATION	WORTH	LOVE & ACCEPTANCE	GRATITUDE	GENEROSITY	ABUNDANCE

What time is it?

GOD ALONE KNOWS THE SECRET PLAN OF THE THINGS HE WILL DO FOR THE WORLD USING MY HAND.

— Toyohiko Kagawa

AUGUST 6

CREATION	WORTH	LOVE & ACCEPTANCE	GRATITUDE	GENEROSITY	ABUNDANCE

The universe is always saying yes, it only says yes. What is it saying yes to?

THE KNOWLEDGE THAT THERE IS A CENTRAL CHAMBER OF THE SOUL, BLAZING WITH THE LIGHT OF DIVINE LOVE AND WISDOM, HAS COME, IN THE COURSE OF HISTORY, TO MULTITUDES OF HUMAN BEINGS. -Aldous Huxley

AUGUST 7

CREATION	WORTH	LOVE & ACCEPTANCE	GRATITUDE	GENEROSITY	ABUNDANCE

Does a drop stay still in the ocean?

IN MOMENTS OF DEEPEST REALIZATION, THE GREAT MYSTICS HAVE SENSED THAT ONE LIFE FLOWS THROUGH ALL AND THAT ALL ARE SOME PART OF THAT LIFE. —Ernest Holmes

AUGUST 8

CREATION	WORTH	LOVE & ACCEPTANCE	GRATITUDE	GENEROSITY	ABUNDANCE

Say out loud three times to yourself: "I am worthy of everything."

THIS MOMENT IS ALL THAT IS.

-Rumi

AUGUST 9

CREATION	WORTH	LOVE & ACCEPTANCE	GRATITUDE	GENEROSITY	ABUNDANCE

Answer the following:
I am open to receiving

_____.

WHAT EVER YOU PROTECT YOU LOSE.

-Matthew Engelhart

AUGUST 10

CREATION	WORTH	LOVE & ACCEPTANCE	GRATITUDE	GENEROSITY	ABUNDANCE

How are you an artist?

IT IS IMPOSSIBLE TO REALIZE GOD AS LONG AS ONE HAS IN MIND A PURPOSE OR OBJECT OTHER THAN REALIZING GOD.

-Joel Goldsmith

CREATION	WORTH	LOVE & ACCEPTANCE	GRATITUDE	GENEROSITY	ABUNDANCE

What is an outcome you are attached to having, or a result you are trying to achieve?

UNLESS I LOVE SOMETHING, IT WILL NOT REVEAL ITSELF TO ME, AND EVERY REVELATION WILL FILL ME WITH THANKFULNESS, FOR I AM MADE RICHER BY IT.
-Rudolph Steiner

AUGUST 12

CREATION	WORTH	LOVE & ACCEPTANCE	GRATITUDE	GENEROSITY	ABUNDANCE

What are five things you are grateful for right now?

LET YOURSELF BE SILENTLY DRAWN BY THE STRONGER PULL OF WHAT YOU REALLY LOVE.

-Rumi

AUGUST 13

CREATION	WORTH	LOVE & ACCEPTANCE	GRATITUDE	GENEROSITY	ABUNDANCE

Say outloud three times:

"I am being love now!"

WHAT COULD THERE BE TO FEAR IN A WORLD THAT I HAVE FORGIVEN AND THAT HAS FORGIVEN ME?

—A Course In Miracles

AUGUST 14

CREATION	WORTH	LOVE & ACCEPTANCE	GRATITUDE	GENEROSITY	ABUNDANCE

Are you proud of your relationship with money?

WHAT THINGS SOEVER YE DESIRE, WHEN YE PRAY, BELIEVE THAT YE RECEIVE THEM, AND YE SHALL HAVE THEM. - *Mark 11:24*

AUGUST 15

CREATION	WORTH	LOVE & ACCEPTANCE	GRATITUDE	GENEROSITY	ABUNDANCE

Can you give up blame?

AN ATTITUDE OF GRATITUDE IS MOST SALUTARY, AND BESPEAKS THE REALIZATION THAT WE ARE NOW IN HEAVEN.

-Ernest Holmes

AUGUST 16

CREATION	WORTH	LOVE & ACCEPTANCE	GRATITUDE	GENEROSITY	ABUNDANCE

What can you be grateful for now that perhaps at one time you resisted or resented?

I AM ENOUGH OF AN ARTIST TO DRAW FREELY UPON MY IMAGINATION. IMAGINATION IS MORE IMPORTANT THAN KNOWLEDGE. KNOWLEDGE IS LIMITED. IMAGINATION ENCIRCLES THE WORLD. —Albert Einstein

AUGUST 17

CREATION	WORTH	LOVE & ACCEPTANCE	GRATITUDE	GENEROSITY	ABUNDANCE

Where do you invest more attention, being grateful or chasing desires?

EACH CHOICE WE MAKE CAUSES A RIPPLE EFFECT IN OUR LIVES. WHEN THINGS HAPPEN TO US, IT IS THE REACTION WE CHOOSE THAT CAN CREATE THE DIFFERENCE BETWEEN THE SORROWS OF OUR PAST AND THE JOY IN OUR FUTURE.
-Chelle Thompson

AUGUST 18

CREATION	WORTH	LOVE & ACCEPTANCE	GRATITUDE	GENEROSITY	ABUNDANCE

What if you started saying "I choose" instead of "I need?"

YE SHALL KNOW THE TRUTH, AND THE TRUTH SHALL MAKE YOU FREE.

-John 8:32

AUGUST 19

CREATION	WORTH	LOVE & ACCEPTANCE	GRATITUDE	GENEROSITY	ABUNDANCE

Say outloud three times:

"I love ____(Spirit Word)____ as my life and as all of life."

THE WONDERFUL ORDERING OF THE SUN, THE
PLANETS, AND THE COMETS CANNOT BUT BE THE
WORK OF AN INTELLIGENT, ALL-POWERFUL BEING.
-Isaac Newton

AUGUST 20

CREATION	WORTH	LOVE & ACCEPTANCE	GRATITUDE	GENEROSITY	ABUNDANCE

What inspires you to
start your day off
powerfully?

SOMEDAY, AFTER WE HAVE MASTERED THE WINDS, THE WAVES, THE TIDES AND GRAVITY, WE SHALL HARNESS THE ENERGIES OF LOVE. THEN, FOR THE SECOND TIME IN THE HISTORY OF THE WORLD, WE WILL HAVE DISCOVERED FIRE.
— Pierre Tielhard de Chardin

AUGUST 21

CREATION	WORTH	LOVE & ACCEPTANCE	GRATITUDE	GENEROSITY	ABUNDANCE

How about saying "I have a full life" rather than "I don't have enough time"?

WE MUST BE THE CHANGE WE WISH TO SEE IN THE WORLD.
-Gandhi

AUGUST 22

CREATION	WORTH	LOVE & ACCEPTANCE	GRATITUDE	GENEROSITY	ABUNDANCE

What could you do today to awaken more fully?

DECIDE BUT TO ACCEPT YOUR RIGHTFUL PLACE
AS CO-CREATOR OF THE UNIVERSE, AND ALL
YOU THINK YOU MADE WILL DISAPPEAR.

- The Course in Miracles

AUGUST 23

CREATION	WORTH	LOVE & ACCEPTANCE	GRATITUDE	GENEROSITY	ABUNDANCE

Who could you acknowledge right now?

WHATEVER THE MIND HOLDS TO AND FIRMLY BELIEVES IN,
FORMS A NEW PATTERN OF THOUGHT WITHIN ITS CREATIVE
MOLD, AS WHATEVER THOUGHT IS HELD IN THE MIND TENDS
TO TAKE OUTWARD FORM IN NEW CREATIONS. -Ernest Holmes

AUGUST 24

CREATION	WORTH	LOVE & ACCEPTANCE	GRATITUDE	GENEROSITY	ABUNDANCE

What opportunity is right in front of you?

AND FORGET NOT THAT THE EARTH DELIGHTS TO
FEEL YOUR BARE FEET AND THE WINDS LONG TO
PLAY WITH YOUR HAIR.
                                        -Kahlil Gibran

AUGUST 25

CREATION	WORTH	LOVE & ACCEPTANCE	GRATITUDE	GENEROSITY	ABUNDANCE

Can you stay in the moment?

IF THE BELOVED IS EVERYWHERE, THE LOVER
IS A VEIL, BUT WHEN LIVING ITSELF BECOMES
THE FRIEND, LOVERS DISAPPEAR. —Rumi

AUGUST 26

CREATION	WORTH	LOVE & ACCEPTANCE	GRATITUDE	GENEROSITY	ABUNDANCE

Say outloud three times: "I am completely fulfilled now!"

WHEN I AM UPSET, IT IS ALWAYS BECAUSE I HAVE REPLACED REALITY WITH ILLUSIONS I MADE UP. THE ILLUSIONS ARE UPSETTING ME BECAUSE I HAVE GIVEN THEM REALITY, AND THUS REGARD REALITY AS AN ILLUSION.
— *A Course in Miracles*

AUGUST 27

CREATION	WORTH	LOVE & ACCEPTANCE	GRATITUDE	GENEROSITY	ABUNDANCE

When you face your fears can you see you are more powerful?

THERE IS SOMETHING IN THIS ATTITUDE OF THANKSGIVING THAT CARRIES US BEYOND THE FIELD OF DOUBT INTO ONE OF PERFECT FAITH AND ACCEPTANCE, RECEPTIVITY...REALIZATION.

-Ernest Holmes

AUGUST 28

CREATION	WORTH	LOVE & ACCEPTANCE	GRATITUDE	GENEROSITY	ABUNDANCE

How could you take on being a better receiver?

LET ONE THEREFORE KEEP THE MIND PURE,
FOR WHAT A MAN THINKS, THAT HE
BECOMES.

-The Upanishads

AUGUST 29

CREATION	WORTH	LOVE & ACCEPTANCE	GRATITUDE	GENEROSITY	ABUNDANCE

What way of being do you most admire in others?

EXPECTATION REDUCES THE JOY IN LIFE.

-Sri Sri Ravi Shankar

AUGUST **30**

CREATION	WORTH	LOVE & ACCEPTANCE	GRATITUDE	GENEROSITY	ABUNDANCE

What are you not saying?

NOT BY WHICH THE EYE SEES
BUT BY WHICH THE EYE CAN
SEE.
                    -The Upanishads

AUGUST 31

CREATION	WORTH	LOVE & ACCEPTANCE	GRATITUDE	GENEROSITY	ABUNDANCE

How could you
embrace your
awakening today?

REAMS
ARE ILLUSTRATION
. . .
from
the book
your soul
is writing
about you.

~Marsha Norman

Impermanence is a principle of harmony. When we do not struggle against it, we are in harmony with reality.
         -PEMA CHODRON

SEPTEMBER 1

CREATION	WORTH	LOVE & ACCEPTANCE	GRATITUDE	GENEROSITY	ABUNDANCE

HOW ABOUT GIVING SOMETHING AWAY TO A STRANGER TODAY?

Virgo Libra

Terrible or not, difficult or not, the only thing that is beautiful, noble, religious, and mystical is to be happy.

-ARNAUD DESJARDINS

SEPTEMBER

2

CREATION	WORTH	LOVE & ACCEPTANCE	GRATITUDE	GENEROSITY	ABUNDANCE

Libra

Virgo

HOW COULD YOU BE MORE GENEROUS?

Whether we regard our situation as heaven or as hell depends on our perception.
-PEMA CHODRON

SEPTEMBER 3

CREATION	WORTH	LOVE & ACCEPTANCE	GRATITUDE	GENEROSITY	ABUNDANCE

WHAT IS ONE THING YOU COULD FORGIVE YOURSELF FOR?

To see the preciousness of all things, we must bring our full attention to life.

-JACK KORNFIELD

SEPTEMBER 4

CREATION	WORTH	LOVE & ACCEPTANCE	GRATITUDE	GENEROSITY	ABUNDANCE

WHERE COULD YOU LET GO OF BEING RIGHT?

Libra

Virgo

Each individual is master of his or her destiny: it is up to each person to create the causes of happiness.

-THE 14TH DALAI LAMA

SEPTEMBER

5

CREATION	WORTH	LOVE & ACCEPTANCE	GRATITUDE	GENEROSITY	ABUNDANCE

Libra

Virgo

HOW COULD YOU MORE FULLY LIVE YOUR PASSION?

Whatever you love you are.

-RUMI

SEPTEMBER

6

CREATION	WORTH	LOVE & ACCEPTANCE	GRATITUDE	GENEROSITY	ABUNDANCE

WHO COULD YOU ACKNOWLEDGE TODAY?

I can escape from this by giving up attack thoughts.

-A COURSE IN MIRACLES

SEPTEMBER

7

CREATION	WORTH	LOVE & ACCEPTANCE	GRATITUDE	GENEROSITY	ABUNDANCE

HOW COULD YOU TAKE ON SURPRISING AND DELIGHTING THOSE AROUND YOU?

Virgo Libra

To be human is to be born into scarcity, not enough love, money, beauty, time... It is not personal.

-MATTHEW ENGELHART

SEPTEMBER

8

CREATION	WORTH	LOVE & ACCEPTANCE	GRATITUDE	GENEROSITY	ABUNDANCE

Libra

Virgo

WHAT DO YOU APPRECIATE ABOUT YOUR FAMILY?

The things that matter most in our lives are not fantastic or grand. They are moments when we touch each other. —Jack Kornfield

SEPTEMBER

9

CREATION	WORTH	LOVE & ACCEPTANCE	GRATITUDE	GENEROSITY	ABUNDANCE

WHAT STORY ABOUT YOUR LIFE COULD YOU RE-CREATE AS MORE POWERFUL?

Libra

Virgo

One who strives to attain Enlightenment must expect to encounter terrible obstacles: anger, desire, mental confusion, pride, and jealousy.

-DILGO KHYENTSE RINPOCHE

SEPTEMBER 10

CREATION	WORTH	LOVE & ACCEPTANCE	GRATITUDE	GENEROSITY	ABUNDANCE

WHO COULD YOU CELEBRATE TODAY?

Libra

Virgo

Truth can have no opposite.
-A Course in Miracles

SEPTEMBER 11

CREATION	WORTH	LOVE & ACCEPTANCE	GRATITUDE	GENEROSITY	ABUNDANCE

Libra

Virgo

WHAT IS ONE WANT YOU COULD LET GO OF TODAY?

We must look at our life without sentimentality, exaggeration or idealism. Does what we are choosing reflect what we most deeply value?
-JACK KORNFIELD

SEPTEMBER

12

CREATION	WORTH	LOVE & ACCEPTANCE	GRATITUDE	GENEROSITY	ABUNDANCE

Libra

Virgo

WHAT IS ONE MIRACLE YOU HAVE EXPERIENCED RECENTLY?

Learning to live is learning to let go.

-SOGYAL RINPOCHE

SEPTEMBER 13

CREATION	WORTH	LOVE & ACCEPTANCE	GRATITUDE	GENEROSITY	ABUNDANCE

Libra

Virgo

SAY OUTLOUD THREE TIMES:

"I AM PEACEFUL KNOWING I AM ALWAYS PROVIDED FOR."

Want what you have and do not want what you do not have. Here you will find true fulfillment.

-JACK KORNFIELD

SEPTEMBER

14

CREATION	WORTH	LOVE & ACCEPTANCE	GRATITUDE	GENEROSITY	ABUNDANCE

WITH WHOM COULD YOU BE MORE WELCOMING?

The art of happiness begins with developing an understanding of what are the truest sources of happiness, and setting our priorities in life based on the cultivation of those sources.

-THE 14TH DALAI LAMA

CREATION	WORTH	LOVE & ACCEPTANCE	GRATITUDE	GENEROSITY	ABUNDANCE

WHAT COULD YOU GIVE UP TRYING TO FIX ABOUT YOU?

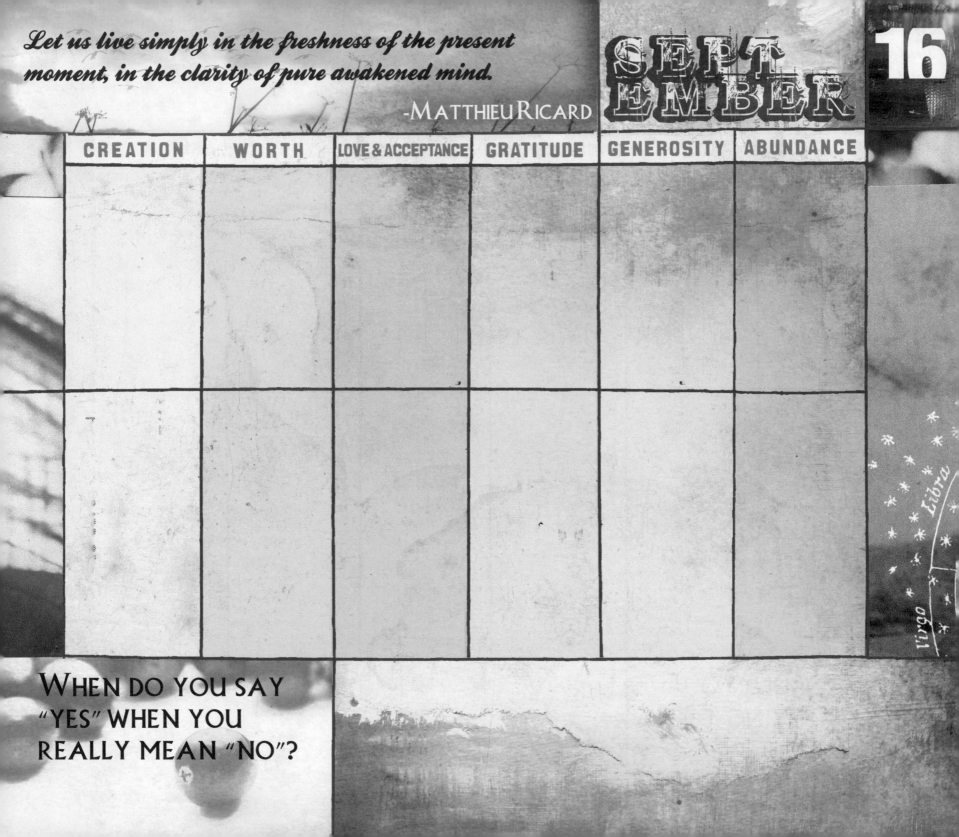

Let us live simply in the freshness of the present moment, in the clarity of pure awakened mind.

-MATTHIEU RICARD

CREATION	WORTH	LOVE & ACCEPTANCE	GRATITUDE	GENEROSITY	ABUNDANCE

Libra

Virgo

WHEN DO YOU SAY "YES" WHEN YOU REALLY MEAN "NO"?

You cannot stop the waves, but you can learn how to surf.

—Joseph Goldstein

SEPTEMBER 17

CREATION	WORTH	LOVE & ACCEPTANCE	GRATITUDE	GENEROSITY	ABUNDANCE

Libra

Virgo

WHAT IS ONE COMPLAINT YOU HAVE THAT YOU COULD LET GO OF?

We have only now, only this single eternal moment opening and unfolding before us, day and night.
-JACK KORNFIELD

SEPTEMBER

18

CREATION	WORTH	LOVE & ACCEPTANCE	GRATITUDE	GENEROSITY	ABUNDANCE

WRITE SOMETHING THAT IS COMPLETELY AUTHENTIC FOR YOU.

It is our mind, and that alone, that chains us or sets us free.
-Dilgo Khyentse Rinpoche

SEPTEMBER 19

CREATION	WORTH	LOVE & ACCEPTANCE	GRATITUDE	GENEROSITY	ABUNDANCE

Libra

Virgo

SAY OUTLOUD THREE TIMES:

"I TRUST (SPIRIT WORD)

AS MY LIFE AND AS ALL OF LIFE."

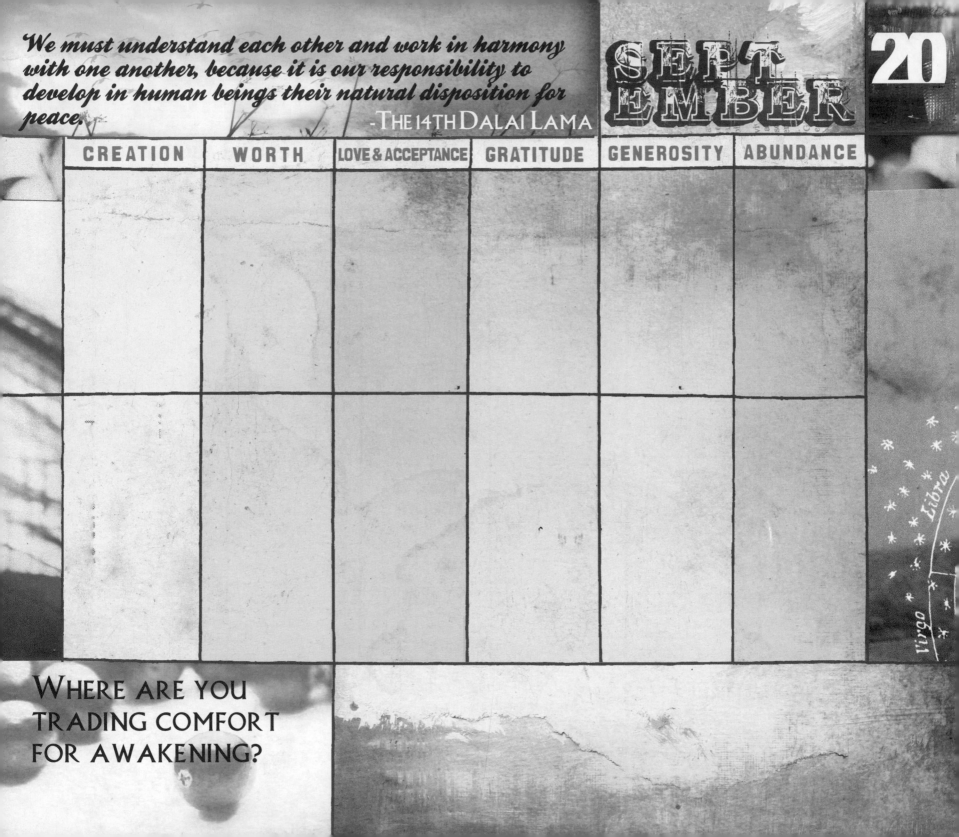

We must understand each other and work in harmony with one another, because it is our responsibility to develop in human beings their natural disposition for peace.

—THE 14TH DALAI LAMA

SEPTEMBER 20

CREATION	WORTH	LOVE & ACCEPTANCE	GRATITUDE	GENEROSITY	ABUNDANCE

Libra

Virgo

WHERE ARE YOU TRADING COMFORT FOR AWAKENING?

There is beauty to be found in the changing of the Earth's seasons, and an inner grace in honouring the cycles of life.
-JACK KORNFIELD

SEPTEMBER

21

CREATION	WORTH	LOVE & ACCEPTANCE	GRATITUDE	GENEROSITY	ABUNDANCE

Libra

Virgo

WHO COULD YOU THANK TODAY?

Creation is a cheerleader, a champion for and of itSelf and all its parts.
-MATTHEW ENGELHART

SEPTEMBER 22

CREATION	WORTH	LOVE & ACCEPTANCE	GRATITUDE	GENEROSITY	ABUNDANCE

Libra

Virgo

WHAT BLESSING
COULD YOU
ACKNOWLEDGE
TODAY?

We will never again have the chance
to be born into a body like this one.
-Kalu Rinpoche

SEPTEMBER

23

CREATION	WORTH	LOVE & ACCEPTANCE	GRATITUDE	GENEROSITY	ABUNDANCE

WHERE ARE YOU NOT
FULLY EXPRESSING
YOUR LOVE?

Libra

Virgo

All of spiritual practice is a matter of relationship: to ourselves, to others, to life's situations.

-JACK KORNFIELD

SEPTEMBER

24

CREATION	WORTH	LOVE & ACCEPTANCE	GRATITUDE	GENEROSITY	ABUNDANCE

Libra

Virgo

WHO COULD YOU FORGIVE TODAY?

Like the birds that gather in the treetops at night and scatter in all directions at the coming of dawn, Phenomena are important.

-SHABKAR

SEPTEMBER

25

CREATION	WORTH	LOVE & ACCEPTANCE	GRATITUDE	GENEROSITY	ABUNDANCE

Libra

Virgo

WHAT IS BEAUTIFUL ABOUT YOU?

This tool, our body, is given to us for only a short time: this life.

-DILGO KHYENTSE RINPOCHE

SEPTEMBER

26

CREATION	WORTH	LOVE & ACCEPTANCE	GRATITUDE	GENEROSITY	ABUNDANCE

Libra

Virgo

SAY OUTLOUD THREE TIMES:
"I GIVE UP RESISTING MYSELF
AND MY WORLD, I CHOOSE
(SPIRIT WORD)'S PERFECTION NOW!

Why, if we are as pragmatic as we claim, do not we begin to ask ourselves seriously: Where does our real future lie? —SOGYAL RINPOCHE

CREATION	WORTH	LOVE & ACCEPTANCE	GRATITUDE	GENEROSITY	ABUNDANCE

Libra

Virgo

WHAT CAN YOU GIVE AWAY TODAY?

We can awaken to basic goodness, our birthright.

-Pema Chodron

SEPTEMBER

28

CREATION	WORTH	LOVE & ACCEPTANCE	GRATITUDE	GENEROSITY	ABUNDANCE

Libra · Virgo

WHAT OPPORTUNITIES FOR AWAKENING ARE YOU CURRENTLY EXPERIENCING?

Who am I?
Who is carrying this body?
-JACK KORNFIELD

SEPTEMBER

29

CREATION	WORTH	LOVE & ACCEPTANCE	GRATITUDE	GENEROSITY	ABUNDANCE

WHAT ARE YOU IN
SERVICE TO?

Libra

Virgo

Our five senses are like openings through which we receive all the perceptions that are then transformed into concepts and ideas.
-ARNAUD DESJARDINS

SEPTEMBER

30

CREATION	WORTH	LOVE & ACCEPTANCE	GRATITUDE	GENEROSITY	ABUNDANCE

WHAT DO YOU LOVE ABOUT MUSIC?

Libra

Virgo

Wake at dawn with a winged heart
and give thanks for another day of loving.
-Kahlil Gibran

CONFIDENCE IS CLOSELY LINKED TO HOW WELL OUR PERCEPTIONS MATCH REALITY.

-matthieu ricard

OCTOBER 1

CREATION	WORTH	LOVE & ACCEPTANCE	GRATITUDE	GENEROSITY	ABUNDANCE

what can you celebrate today?

A BRIDGE IS REVEALED WHICH CONNECTS
THE EVERYDAY TEMPORAL WORLD OF SENSE
PERCEPTIONS TO THE REALM OF TIMELESS
KNOWLEDGE.
                    -Lama anagarika Govinda

OCTOBER 2

CREATION	WORTH	LOVE & ACCEPTANCE	GRATITUDE	GENEROSITY	ABUNDANCE

what are you
resisting facing in
your life?

OUR CONSCIOUSNESS CONTAINS ALL THESE
ROLES AND MORE: THE HERO AND THE LOVER,
THE HERMIT, THE DICTATOR, THE WISE
WOMAN AND THE FOOL.
-jack kornfield

OCTOBER 3

CREATION	WORTH	LOVE & ACCEPTANCE	GRATITUDE	GENEROSITY	ABUNDANCE

what freedom do
you wish you had?

WE ARE THE SUM OF A HUGE NUMBER OF FREE ACTIONS FOR WHICH WE ARE THE ONLY ONES RESPONSIBLE.

-matthieu ricard
and trinh xuan thuan

CREATION	WORTH	LOVE & ACCEPTANCE	GRATITUDE	GENEROSITY	ABUNDANCE

HOW COULD YOU BE
a better receiver?

ACTIONS MAY BE POSITIVE OR NEGATIVE ACCORDING TO THE INTENTION THAT UNDERLIES THEM, JUST AS A CRYSTAL REFRACTS THE COLOURS OF ITS SURROUNDINGS.   -dilgo khyentse rinpoche

OCTOBER 5

CREATION	WORTH	LOVE & ACCEPTANCE	GRATITUDE	GENEROSITY	ABUNDANCE

can you see that your access to love is through being loving?

IT IS ONLY THROUGH CONSTANT TRAINING
THAT OUR PRACTICE WILL GROW STEADY
AND WE WILL BE ABLE TO CONTROL OUR
NEGATIVE TENDENCIES FEARLESSLY.

-dilgo khyentse rinpoche

OCTOBER 6

CREATION	WORTH	LOVE & ACCEPTANCE	GRATITUDE	GENEROSITY	ABUNDANCE

can you see that your
wounds are simply an
opportunity to heal
yourself?

WHEN WE FEEL RESPONSIBLE, CONCERNED, AND COMMITTED, WE BEGIN TO FEEL DEEP EMOTION AND GREAT COURAGE.
-THE 14TH DALAI LAMA

OCTOBER 7

CREATION	WORTH	LOVE & ACCEPTANCE	GRATITUDE	GENEROSITY	ABUNDANCE

do you know that love only exists in the present moment?

WE CAN BRING AN OPEN AND
RESPECTFUL ATTENTION TO THE
SENSATIONS THAT MAKE UP OUR BODILY
EXPERIENCE. -jack kornfield

OCTOBER 8

CREATION	WORTH	LOVE & ACCEPTANCE	GRATITUDE	GENEROSITY	ABUNDANCE

what fear are you
resisting facing?

IF WE KNEW THAT TONIGHT WE WERE GOING TO GO BLIND, WE WOULD TAKE A LONGING, LAST REAL LOOK AT EVERY BLADE OF GRASS, EVERY CLOUD FORMATION, EVERY SPECK OF DUST, EVERY RAINBOW, RAINDROP – EVERYTHING. -pema chodron

OCTOBER 9

	CREATION	WORTH	LOVE & ACCEPTANCE	GRATITUDE	GENEROSITY	ABUNDANCE

what if your life is unfolding perfectly?

TOUCH IS THE VEHICLE THROUGH WHICH WE COMFORT ONE ANOTHER AND ARE COMFORTED, VIA HUGS OR CLASPS OF THE HAND.

-quoted by THE 14TH DALAI LAMA

OCTOBER 10

CREATION	WORTH	LOVE & ACCEPTANCE	GRATITUDE	GENEROSITY	ABUNDANCE

WHAT aspect of YOURSELF could YOU MORE FULLY embrace?

OCTOBER 11

WHEN ONE INTENDS TO MOVE OR SPEAK, ONE SHOULD FIRST EXAMINE ONE'S OWN MIND AND THEN ACT APPROPRIATELY WITH COMPOSURE.

-SHantideva

CREATION	WORTH	LOVE & ACCEPTANCE	GRATITUDE	GENEROSITY	ABUNDANCE

what new freedom can you celebrate today?

THE ORDINARY MIND IS THE CEASELESSLY SHIFTING AND SHIFTLESS PREY OF EXTERNAL INFLUENCES, HABITUAL TENDENCIES, AND CONDITIONING: THE MASTERS LIKEN IT TO A CANDLE FLAME IN AN OPEN DOORWAY, VULNERABLE TO ALL THE WINDS OF CIRCUMSTANCE. -SOGYAL RINPOCHE

OCTOBER 1 2

CREATION	WORTH	LOVE & ACCEPTANCE	GRATITUDE	GENEROSITY	ABUNDANCE

where is love expanding you in your life?

IT IS THE PLACE OF FEELING THAT BINDS US OR FREES US.

-jack kornfield

CREATION	WORTH	LOVE & ACCEPTANCE	GRATITUDE	GENEROSITY	ABUNDANCE

say out loud three times:
"I love being grateful.
I love being generous."

INSTEAD OF ALLOWING OURSELVES TO BE
LED AND TRAPPED BY OUR FEELINGS, WE
SHOULD LET THEM DISAPPEAR AS SOON AS
THEY FORM, LIKE LETTERS DRAWN ON
WATER WITH A FINGER. -dilgo khyentse rinpoche

OCTOBER 14

CREATION	WORTH	LOVE & ACCEPTANCE	GRATITUDE	GENEROSITY	ABUNDANCE

how are you
awakening today?

UNTIL WE STOP CLINGING TO THE CONCEPT OF
GOOD AND EVIL, THE WORLD WILL CONTINUE
TO MANIFEST AS FRIENDLY GODDESSES AND
HARMFUL DEMONS.
-pema chodron

OCTOBER 15

CREATION	WORTH	LOVE & ACCEPTANCE	GRATITUDE	GENEROSITY	ABUNDANCE

what would you love
to be acknowledged
for?

THE CREATIONS OF THE MIND ARE MORE
NUMEROUS THAN SPECKS OF DUST IN A
RAY OF SUNLIGHT.
-milarepa

OCTOBER 16

CREATION	WORTH	LOVE & ACCEPTANCE	GRATITUDE	GENEROSITY	ABUNDANCE

HOW COULD YOU MORE
FULLY BE HERE NOW?

OCTOBER

17

THE BASIC ROOT OF HAPPINESS LIES IN OUR MINDS. OUTER CIRCUMSTANCES ARE NOTHING MORE THAN ADVERSE OR FAVOURABLE.

-matthieu ricard

CREATION	WORTH	LOVE & ACCEPTANCE	GRATITUDE	GENEROSITY	ABUNDANCE

HOW Have you Been provided for today?

THE MIND IN ITS NATURAL STATE CAN
BE COMPARED TO THE SKY, COVERED BY
LAYERS OF CLOUDS WHICH HIDE ITS
TRUE NATURE.
                                    -kalu Rinpoche

OCTOBER

18

CREATION	WORTH	LOVE & ACCEPTANCE	GRATITUDE	GENEROSITY	ABUNDANCE

what miracle has
happened in your life
recently?

DO NOT ENCUMBER YOUR MIND WITH USELESS THOUGHTS. WHAT GOOD DOES IT DO TO BROOD ON THE PAST OR ANTICIPATE THE FUTURE? REMAIN IN THE SIMPLICITY OF THE PRESENT MOMENT. -dilgo khyentse rinpoche

OCTOBER 19

	CREATION	WORTH	LOVE & ACCEPTANCE	GRATITUDE	GENEROSITY	ABUNDANCE

say out loud three times:

"i love contributing to everyone."

WE CAN BRING OUR SPIRITUAL PRACTICE INTO
THE STREETS, INTO OUR COMMUNITIES, WHEN
WE SEE EACH REALM AS A TEMPLE, AS A
PLACE TO DISCOVER THAT WHICH IS SACRED.
-jack kornfield

OCTOBER 20

CREATION	WORTH	LOVE & ACCEPTANCE	GRATITUDE	GENEROSITY	ABUNDANCE

what is perfect about
this moment?

SOMEHOW, IN THE PROCESS OF TRYING TO DENY
THAT THINGS ARE ALWAYS CHANGING, WE LOSE
OUR SENSE OF THE SACREDNESS OF LIFE. WE TEND
TO FORGET THAT WE ARE PART OF THE NATURAL
SCHEME OF THINGS.   -pema chodron

OCTOBER

21

CREATION	WORTH	LOVE & ACCEPTANCE	GRATITUDE	GENEROSITY	ABUNDANCE

can you see that your
access to joy is being
joyful?

LIFE IS EXPRESSED IN A PERPETUAL SEQUENCE OF CHANGES. THE BIRTH OF A CHILD IS THE DEATH OF A BABY, JUST AS THE BIRTH OF THE ADOLESCENT IS THE DEATH OF THE CHILD.

-arnaud desjardins

CREATION	WORTH	LOVE & ACCEPTANCE	GRATITUDE	GENEROSITY	ABUNDANCE

what if you started saying: "i get to" instead of "i have to"?

WHEN FACED WITH A FEELING OF STAGNATION
AND CONFUSION, IT MAY BE HELPFUL TO TAKE AN
HOUR, AN AFTERNOON, OR EVEN SEVERAL DAYS TO
REFLECT ON WHAT IT IS THAT WILL TRULY BRING
US HAPPINESS.
                    -THE 14TH DALAI LAMA

OCTOBER

2
3

CREATION	WORTH	LOVE & ACCEPTANCE	GRATITUDE	GENEROSITY	ABUNDANCE

what inspires you
about the work you
do?

THERE IS NOTHING CLEVER ABOUT NOT BEING HAPPY.

-arnaud desjardins

CREATION	WORTH	LOVE & ACCEPTANCE	GRATITUDE	GENEROSITY	ABUNDANCE

what is perfect about you?

WHAT COUNTS IN NOT THE ENORMITY OF THE TASK, BUT THE SIZE OF THE COURAGE.

-matthieu ricard

OCTOBER 25

CREATION	WORTH	LOVE & ACCEPTANCE	GRATITUDE	GENEROSITY	ABUNDANCE

who can you give up blaming?

FEELINGS LIKE DISAPPOINTMENT, EMBARRASSMENT, IRRITATION, RESENTMENT, ANGER, JEALOUSY, AND FEAR, INSTEAD OF BEING BAD NEWS, ARE ACTUALLY VERY CLEAR MOMENTS THAT TEACH US WHERE IT IS THAT WE ARE HOLDING BACK. -pema chodron

OCTOBER 26

CREATION	WORTH	LOVE & ACCEPTANCE	GRATITUDE	GENEROSITY	ABUNDANCE

say out loud three times: "I choose this sacred moment. there is nowhere to get to."

WE ARE AWAKENED TO THE PROFOUND
REALIZATION THAT THE TRUE PATH TO
LIBERATION IS TO LET GO OF
EVERYTHING.
-jack kornfield

OCTOBER 27

CREATION	WORTH	LOVE & ACCEPTANCE	GRATITUDE	GENEROSITY	ABUNDANCE

what attachment can
you release?

USUALLY WE THINK THAT BRAVE
PEOPLE HAVE NO FEAR. THE TRUTH IS
THAT THEY ARE INTIMATE WITH FEAR.

-pema chodron

OCTOBER

28

CREATION	WORTH	LOVE & ACCEPTANCE	GRATITUDE	GENEROSITY	ABUNDANCE

what is something you
could share?

NOTHING GOES RIGHT ON THE OUTSIDE WHEN NOTHING IS GOING RIGHT ON THE INSIDE.

-matthieu ricard

OCTOBER 29

CREATION	WORTH	LOVE & ACCEPTANCE	GRATITUDE	GENEROSITY	ABUNDANCE

WHO IS YOUR HERO?

THINGS FALLING APART IS A KIND OF TESTING AND ALSO A KIND OF HEALING.
-pema chodron

OCTOBER 30

CREATION	WORTH	LOVE & ACCEPTANCE	GRATITUDE	GENEROSITY	ABUNDANCE

where are you being "it is better over there"?

WHEN THERE'S DISAPPOINTMENT, I DON'T KNOW IF IT'S THE END OF THE STORY. BUT IT MAY BE THE BEGINNING OF A GREAT ADVENTURE. -pema chodron

OCTOBER 31

CREATION	WORTH	LOVE & ACCEPTANCE	GRATITUDE	GENEROSITY	ABUNDANCE

in what area of your life could you be more trusting?

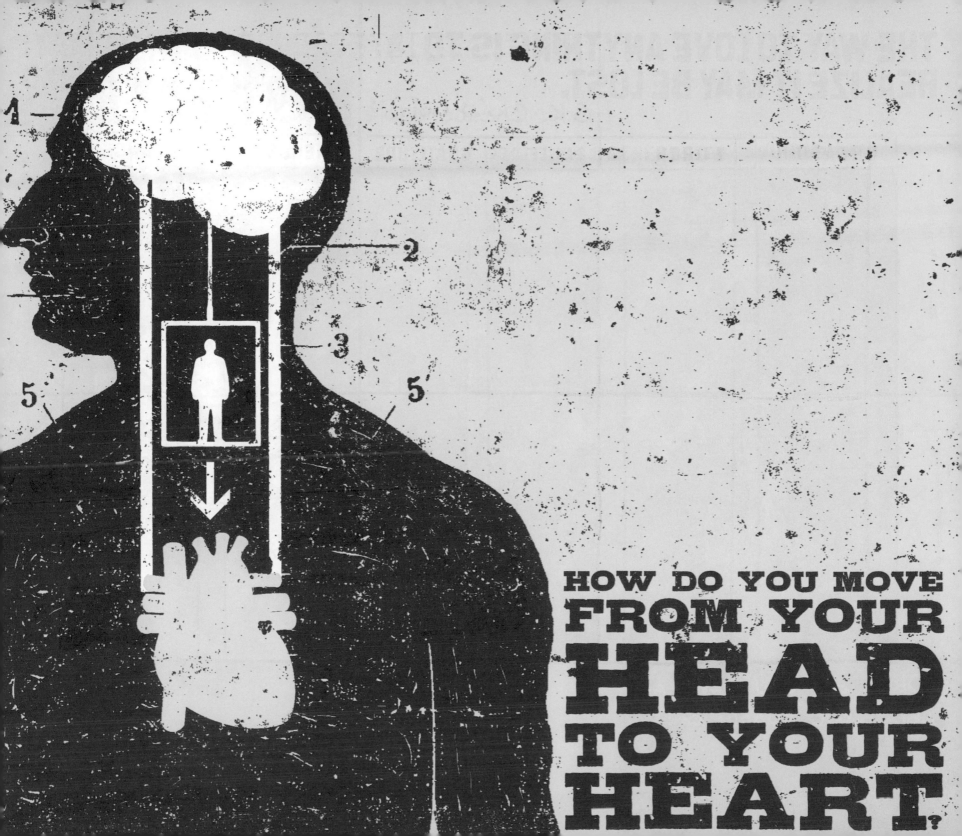

THE WAY TO LOVE ANYTHING IS TO REALIZE IT MAY BE LOST.

-G.K. Chesterton

NOVEMBER 1

CREATION	WORTH	LOVE & ACCEPTANCE	GRATITUDE	GENEROSITY	ABUNDANCE

What do you have an abundant supply of?

THE HEART HAS REASONS THAT REASON DOES NOT KNOW.

-PASCAL

NOVEMBER 2

CREATION	WORTH	LOVE & ACCEPTANCE	GRATITUDE	GENEROSITY	ABUNDANCE

What is your super power?

WHO I AM IS WHAT I HAVE TO GIVE. QUITE SI PLY, I MUST REME BER THIS IS ENOUGH.

-Anne Wilson Schaef

NOVEMBER 3

CREATION	WORTH	LOVE & ACCEPTANCE	GRATITUDE	GENEROSITY	ABUNDANCE

What have you been avoiding taking on?

GOD SPEAKS TO ALL INDIVIDUALS THROUGH WHAT HAPPENS TO THEM MOMENT BY MOMENT. —Jean Pierre De Caussade

NOVEMBER 4

CREATION	WORTH	LOVE & ACCEPTANCE	GRATITUDE	GENEROSITY	ABUNDANCE

Whose beauty overwhelms you?

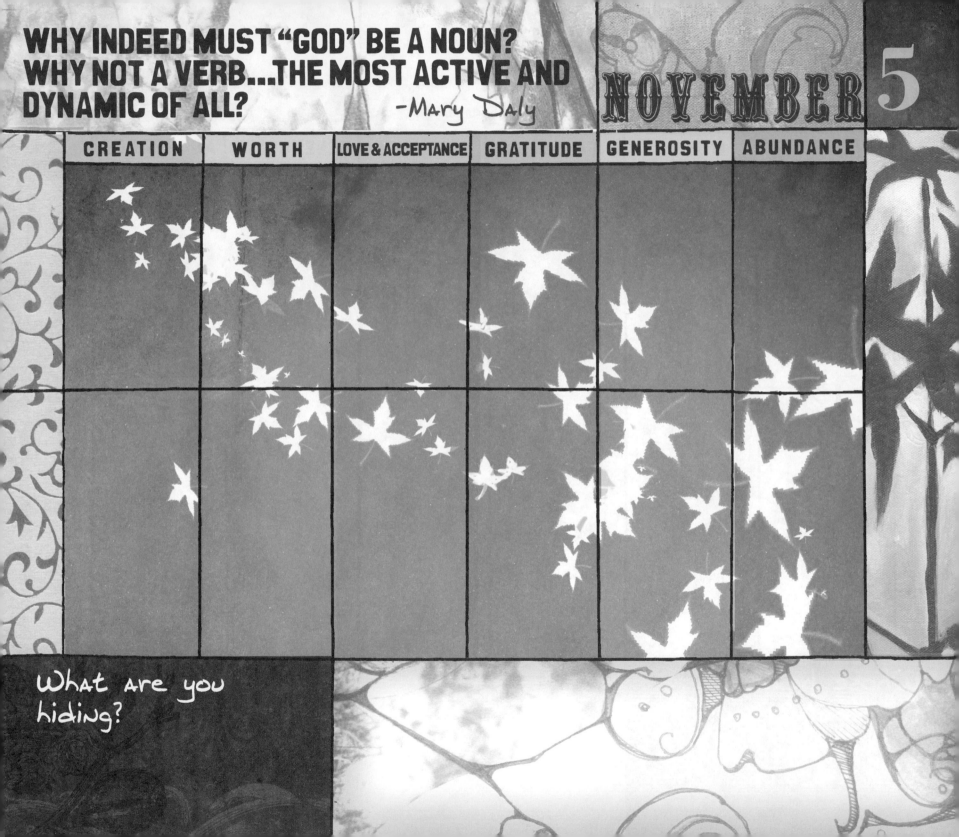

ANALYSIS KILLS SPONTANEITY.

-Amiel

NOVEMBER 6

CREATION	WORTH	LOVE & ACCEPTANCE	GRATITUDE	GENEROSITY	ABUNDANCE

What did you once hold as sacred, that now seems mundane?

WHAT IS MATTER?—NEVERMIND.
WHAT IS MIND?—NO MATTER.

-Punch 29:19

NOVEMBER 7

CREATION	WORTH	LOVE & ACCEPTANCE	GRATITUDE	GENEROSITY	ABUNDANCE

What is working in
your life?

IT TAKES GREAT COURAGE TO BREAK WITH ONE'S PAST HISTORY.

—Marion Woodman

NOVEMBER 8

CREATION	WORTH	LOVE & ACCEPTANCE	GRATITUDE	GENEROSITY	ABUNDANCE

Who has contributed to your life?

WHERE THERE IS MUCH LIGHT, THE SHADOW IS DEEP.

-Johann W. Goethe

NOVEMBER 9

CREATION	WORTH	LOVE & ACCEPTANCE	GRATITUDE	GENEROSITY	ABUNDANCE

Where are you being inflexible?

SOMETIMES YOU JUST NEED TO LOOK REALITY IN THE EYE AND DENY IT.

-Garrison Keillor

NOVEMBER 10

CREATION	WORTH	LOVE & ACCEPTANCE	GRATITUDE	GENEROSITY	ABUNDANCE

Who could you choose to see differently?

BY FAR THE BEST PROOF IS EXPERIENCE.

-Francis Bacon

NOVEMBER II

CREATION	WORTH	LOVE & ACCEPTANCE	GRATITUDE	GENEROSITY	ABUNDANCE

What do you LOVE about the work you do?

A SENSE OF HUMOR REDUCES PEOPLE AND PROBLEMS TO THEIR PROPER PROPORTIONS.

—Arnold Glasow

NOVEMBER 12

CREATION	WORTH	LOVE & ACCEPTANCE	GRATITUDE	GENEROSITY	ABUNDANCE

What gets in the way of you being willing to be clear?

ALTHOUGH THE WORLD IS FULL OF SUFFERING, IT IS ALSO FULL OF OVER COMING IT.

-Helen Keller

NOVEMBER 13

CREATION	WORTH	LOVE & ACCEPTANCE	GRATITUDE	GENEROSITY	ABUNDANCE

Say out loud three times: "I love releasing and receiving, knowing they are one and the same."

EVEN IF YOU'RE ON THE RIGHT TRACK, YOU'LL GET RUN OVER IF YOU JUST SIT THERE.

-Will Rogers

NOVEMBER

14

CREATION	WORTH	LOVE & ACCEPTANCE	GRATITUDE	GENEROSITY	ABUNDANCE

What keeps you from asking for support?

IT'S A FUNNY THING ABOUT LIFE; IF YOU REFUSE TO ACCEPT ANYTHING BUT THE BEST, YOU VERY OFTEN GET IT. —Somerset Maugham

NOVEMBER 15

CREATION	WORTH	LOVE & ACCEPTANCE	GRATITUDE	GENEROSITY	ABUNDANCE

If your life was a billboard, what would it look like or say?

IF YOU WAIT UNTIL YOU'RE SURE, YOU MAY WAIT FOREVER.

-Will Rogers

NOVEMBER 16

CREATION	WORTH	LOVE & ACCEPTANCE	GRATITUDE	GENEROSITY	ABUNDANCE

Who are you making wrong?

PROBLEMS ARE ONLY OPPORTUNITIES IN WORK CLOTHES.

−Henry J. Kaiser

NOVEMBER

17

CREATION	WORTH	LOVE & ACCEPTANCE	GRATITUDE	GENEROSITY	ABUNDANCE

Where are you out of integrity?

DOUBT IS A PAIN TOO LONELY TO KNOW FAITH IS HIS TWIN BROTHER.

–Kahlil Gibran

NOVEMBER 18

CREATION	WORTH	LOVE & ACCEPTANCE	GRATITUDE	GENEROSITY	ABUNDANCE

Who gets how great you are?

DREAMS TAKEN TOO SERIOUSLY BECOME REALITIES.

—Mass Turnpike Billboard

NOVEMBER 19

CREATION	WORTH	LOVE & ACCEPTANCE	GRATITUDE	GENEROSITY	ABUNDANCE

Say out loud three times: "I am grateful for all of life for every expression of _____ (Spirit Word)."

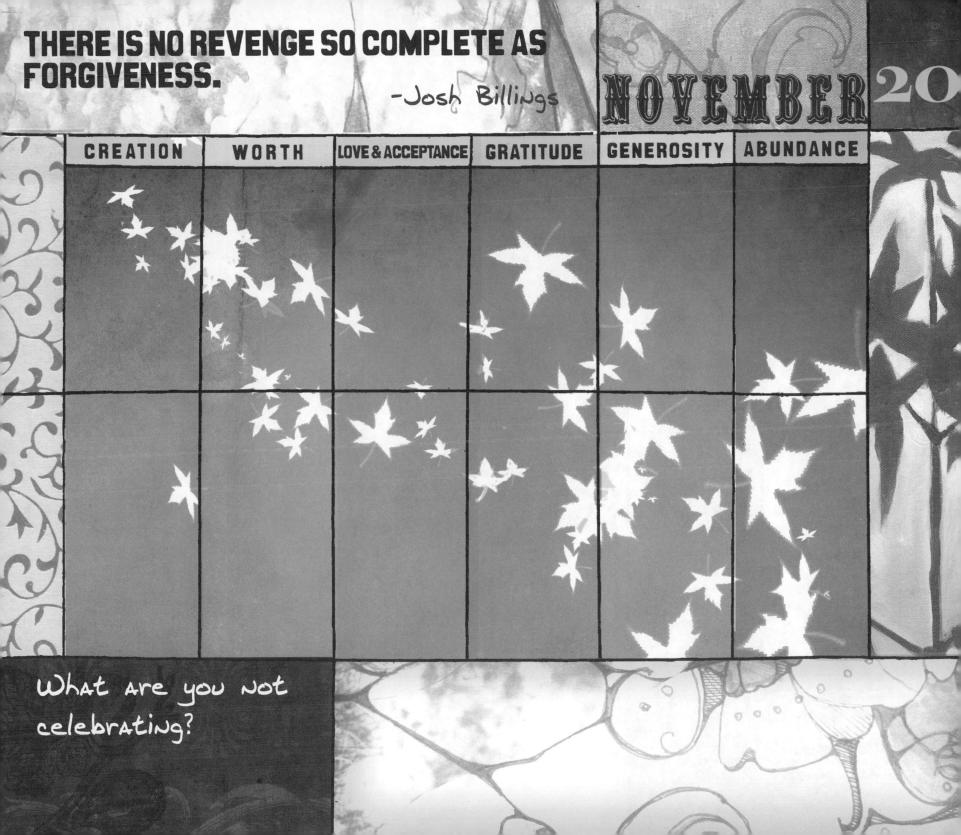

THERE IS NO REVENGE SO COMPLETE AS FORGIVENESS.

-Josh Billings

NOVEMBER 20

CREATION	WORTH	LOVE & ACCEPTANCE	GRATITUDE	GENEROSITY	ABUNDANCE

What are you not celebrating?

THE WAY TO SUCCEED IS TO DOUBLE YOUR FAILURE RATE.

-Thomas Watson

NOVEMBER 21

CREATION	WORTH	LOVE & ACCEPTANCE	GRATITUDE	GENEROSITY	ABUNDANCE

Where are you saying you're unfulfilled?

TROUBLES ARE OFTEN TOOLS BY WHICH GOD FASHIONS US BETTER THINGS.

-H.W. Beecher

NOVEMBER 22

CREATION	WORTH	LOVE & ACCEPTANCE	GRATITUDE	GENEROSITY	ABUNDANCE

What are you trusting?

NO ACT OF KINDNESS, HOWEVER SMALL, IS EVER WASTED.

-Aesop

NOVEMBER 23

CREATION	WORTH	LOVE & ACCEPTANCE	GRATITUDE	GENEROSITY	ABUNDANCE

When do you experience love?

BE KIND; EVERYONE YOU MEET IS FIGHTING A HARD BATTLE.

—John Watson

NOVEMBER **24**

CREATION	WORTH	LOVE & ACCEPTANCE	GRATITUDE	GENEROSITY	ABUNDANCE

If life is about being more unconditionally loving and forgiving, what opportunity do you see for yourself?

WHILE WE TRY TO TEACH OUR CHILDREN ALL ABOUT LIFE, OUR CHILDREN TEACH US WHAT LIFE IS ALL ABOUT. —Angela Schwindt

NOVEMBER 25

CREATION	WORTH	LOVE & ACCEPTANCE	GRATITUDE	GENEROSITY	ABUNDANCE

Where are you being separate?

YOU CANNOT TRULY LISTEN TO SOMEONE AND DO ANYTHING ELSE AT THE SAME TIME.

-M. Scott Peck

NOVEMBER 26

CREATION	WORTH	LOVE & ACCEPTANCE	GRATITUDE	GENEROSITY	ABUNDANCE

Say outloud three times:

"I am thankful for all of life now."

LIFE IS A CONSTANT PRAYER OF GRATITUDE FOR THOSE WHO CHERISH ITS MOMENTS.

-Mary Browne

NOVEMBER 27

CREATION	WORTH	LOVE & ACCEPTANCE	GRATITUDE	GENEROSITY	ABUNDANCE

What are you not fully choosing?

YOU CAN'T HOLD A MAN DOWN WITHOUT STAYING DOWN WITH HIM.

-Booker T. Washington

NOVEMBER 28

CREATION	WORTH	LOVE & ACCEPTANCE	GRATITUDE	GENEROSITY	ABUNDANCE

Where have you overcome fear?

FOUR THOUSAND VOLUMES OF METAPHYSICS WILL NOT TEACH US WHAT THE SOUL IS.
—Voltaire

NOVEMBER 29

CREATION	WORTH	LOVE & ACCEPTANCE	GRATITUDE	GENEROSITY	ABUNDANCE

What gift do you offer the world?

KNOWLEDGE SPEAKS, BUT WISDOM LISTENS.

-Oliver Wendall Holmes

NOVEMBER 30

CREATION	WORTH	LOVE & ACCEPTANCE	GRATITUDE	GENEROSITY	ABUNDANCE

What isn't going as planned?

BY LETTING GO IT ALL GETS DONE.
THE WORLD IS WON BY THOSE WHO LET IT GO.
BUT WHEN YOU TRY AND TRY,
THE WORLD IS BEYOND WINNING.
—LAO TZU

That it will never come again is what makes life so sweet.

-Emily Dickinson

December 1

CREATION	WORTH	LOVE & ACCEPTANCE	GRATITUDE	GENEROSITY	ABUNDANCE

Where has life surprised you?

The strongest principle of growth lies in human choice.

-George Eliot

December 2

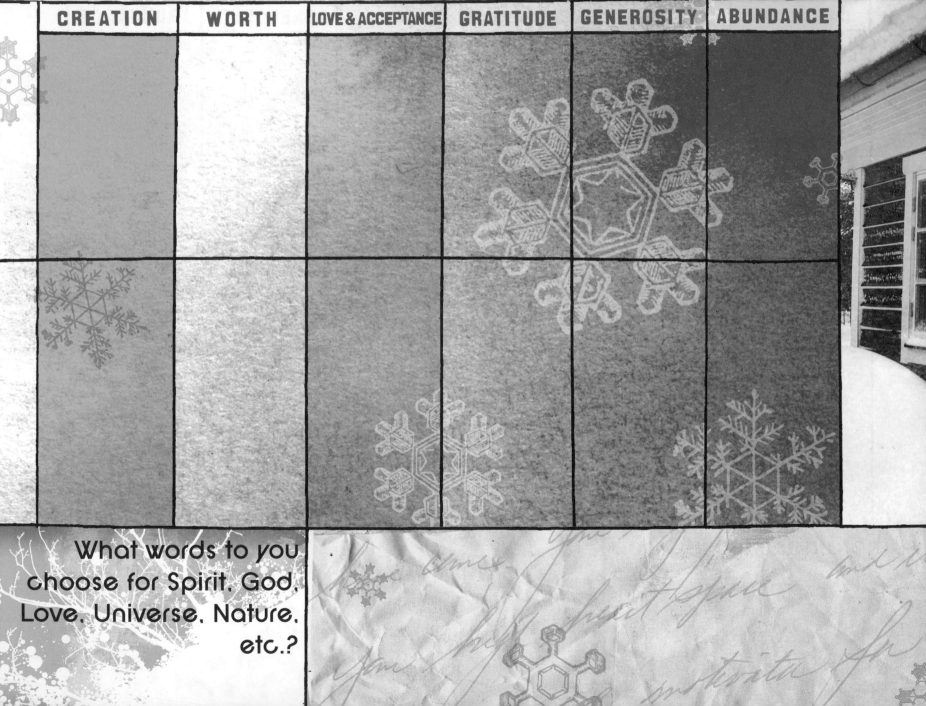

CREATION	WORTH	LOVE & ACCEPTANCE	GRATITUDE	GENEROSITY	ABUNDANCE

What words to you choose for Spirit, God, Love, Universe, Nature, etc.?

A friend is a gift you give yourself.

-Robert Louis Stevenson

December 3

CREATION	WORTH	LOVE & ACCEPTANCE	GRATITUDE	GENEROSITY	ABUNDANCE

What are you saying
isn't fair?

Separate reeds are weak and easily broken; but bound together they are strong and hard to tear apart.
-The Midrash

December 4

CREATION	WORTH	LOVE & ACCEPTANCE	GRATITUDE	GENEROSITY	ABUNDANCE

Where are you playing it safe?

The longing to produce great inspirations, didn't produce anything but more longing.

-Sophie Kerr

December 5

CREATION	WORTH	LOVE & ACCEPTANCE	GRATITUDE	GENEROSITY	ABUNDANCE

Where are you being brave?

I come not to entertain you with worldly festivities but to arouse your sleeping memory of immortality.
-Paramahansa Yogananda

December 6

CREATION	WORTH	LOVE & ACCEPTANCE	GRATITUDE	GENEROSITY	ABUNDANCE

Where are you loving bigger than the circumstance?

Argue for your limitations and sure enough they're yours.

-Richard Bach

December 7

CREATION	WORTH	LOVE & ACCEPTANCE	GRATITUDE	GENEROSITY	ABUNDANCE

When has love surprised you?

Millions pray for immortality who do not know what to do with themselves on a rainy Sunday afternoon.

-Ertz

December 8

CREATION	WORTH	LOVE & ACCEPTANCE	GRATITUDE	GENEROSITY	ABUNDANCE

What's challenging you?

I dream my painting, then I paint my dream.

-Vincent Van Gogh

December 9

CREATION	WORTH	LOVE & ACCEPTANCE	GRATITUDE	GENEROSITY	ABUNDANCE

What inspires you about children?

After silence, that which comes closest to expressing the unexpressible is music.

-Aldous Huxley

December 10

CREATION	WORTH	LOVE & ACCEPTANCE	GRATITUDE	GENEROSITY	ABUNDANCE

Where are you settling for less?

Life is a pure flame, and we live by an invisible sun within us.

-Thomas Browne

December 11

CREATION	WORTH	LOVE & ACCEPTANCE	GRATITUDE	GENEROSITY	ABUNDANCE

Where are your beliefs limiting your potential?

You often meet your destiny on the road you take to avoid it.

-William McFee

December 12

CREATION	WORTH	LOVE & ACCEPTANCE	GRATITUDE	GENEROSITY	ABUNDANCE

Where are you not thinking of the whole?

The eternal quest of the individual human being is to shatter his loneliness.

-JM Barrie

December 13

CREATION	WORTH	LOVE & ACCEPTANCE	GRATITUDE	GENEROSITY	ABUNDANCE

Say out loud three times: "I am enjoying letting go of wants I no longer need."

Remember your humanity and forget the rest.

-Albert Einstein

December 14

CREATION	WORTH	LOVE & ACCEPTANCE	GRATITUDE	GENEROSITY	ABUNDANCE

What is the best about today?

There lives more faith in honest doubt,
believe me, than in half the creeds.
-Lord Alfred Tennyson

December 15

CREATION	WORTH	LOVE & ACCEPTANCE	GRATITUDE	GENEROSITY	ABUNDANCE

Where could you be
more flexible?

Only if we are secure in our beliefs can we see the comical side of the universe.

-Flannery O' Conner

December 16

CREATION	WORTH	LOVE & ACCEPTANCE	GRATITUDE	GENEROSITY	ABUNDANCE

Where is upset an awakening?

We do our best to disprove the fact, but a fact it remains; man is as divine as nature, as infinite as the void.

-Aldous Huxley

December 17

CREATION	WORTH	LOVE & ACCEPTANCE	GRATITUDE	GENEROSITY	ABUNDANCE

When do you give up?

There is no king who has not had a slave among his ancestors, and no slave who has not had a king among his.

-Helen Keller

December 18

CREATION	WORTH	LOVE & ACCEPTANCE	GRATITUDE	GENEROSITY	ABUNDANCE

Where have you broken your word?

We may have all come on different ships, but we're in the same boat now.

-Martin Luther King Jr.

December 19

CREATION	WORTH	LOVE & ACCEPTANCE	GRATITUDE	GENEROSITY	ABUNDANCE

Say out loud three times:
"I am the love of
_____
(Spirit Word)

in expression."

All animals are equal, but some are more equal than others.

-George Orwell

December 20

CREATION	WORTH	LOVE & ACCEPTANCE	GRATITUDE	GENEROSITY	ABUNDANCE

When has a dream come true?

What grows, never grows old.

-Noah Benshea

December 21

CREATION	WORTH	LOVE & ACCEPTANCE	GRATITUDE	GENEROSITY	ABUNDANCE

Where are you comparing yourself to others?

Change really becomes a necessity when we try not to do it.

-Anne Wilson Schaef

December 22

CREATION	WORTH	LOVE & ACCEPTANCE	GRATITUDE	GENEROSITY	ABUNDANCE

How have you exceeded your own expectations?

It's not the mountain we conquer, but ourselves.

-Sir Edmund Hillary

CREATION	WORTH	LOVE & ACCEPTANCE	GRATITUDE	GENEROSITY	ABUNDANCE

What is *your* favorite miracle?

Only the shallow know themselves.

-Oscar Wilde

December 24

CREATION	WORTH	LOVE & ACCEPTANCE	GRATITUDE	GENEROSITY	ABUNDANCE

Where do you say love is missing?

It takes no time to fall in love, but it takes you years to know what love is.

-Jason Mraz

December 25

CREATION	WORTH	LOVE & ACCEPTANCE	GRATITUDE	GENEROSITY	ABUNDANCE

What do your friends love about you?

Nothing is so potent as the silent influence of a good example.

-James Kent

December 26

CREATION	WORTH	LOVE & ACCEPTANCE	GRATITUDE	GENEROSITY	ABUNDANCE

Say out loud three times: "I am deeply grateful for everything I receive and I enjoy giving to others."

You can discover more about a person in an hour of play than in a year of conversation.

-Plato

December 27

CREATION	WORTH	LOVE & ACCEPTANCE	GRATITUDE	GENEROSITY	ABUNDANCE

What is the masterpiece you are working on?

Darkness cannot drive out darkness; only light can do that. Hate cannot drive out hate; only love can do that. —Martin Luther King Jr.

December 28

CREATION	WORTH	LOVE & ACCEPTANCE	GRATITUDE	GENEROSITY	ABUNDANCE

What do *you* appreciate about your father?

Nothing can bring you peace but yourself.

-Ralph Waldo Emerson

December 29

CREATION	WORTH	LOVE & ACCEPTANCE	GRATITUDE	GENEROSITY	ABUNDANCE

How has your family
supported you?

Never give nor take an excuse.

-Florence Nightengale

December 30

CREATION	WORTH	LOVE & ACCEPTANCE	GRATITUDE	GENEROSITY	ABUNDANCE

What do you worship?

Experience is a hard teacher because she gives the test first, the lesson afterwards.
-Oliver Wendall Holmes

December 31

CREATION	WORTH	LOVE & ACCEPTANCE	GRATITUDE	GENEROSITY	ABUNDANCE

Say out loud three times: "Where I keep my attention creates my experience! I now choose to keep my attention on being generous."

Congratulations for exploring the possibility of Plenty of Time!
We would love for you to share your experience with us.

We've set up a specific web address just to hear your feedback.

Please visit:
www.cafegratitude.com/PlentyOfTime
and let us know who you've become.

Thank you for discovering who you get to be!